Working with Dementia

Working with Dementia
Guidelines for Professionals

Editor Mary Marshall

Consultant Publisher Jo Compling

Venture Press

Published by Venture Press
16 Kent Street
Birmingham B5 6RD

First published 1990

Cover illustration: By kind permission of Gill Embleton
and Social Work today.

Design and Production by Saxon Publishing Consultants
Limited
Typeset in 10/11 Baskerville by TecSet Limited

Printed and bound in England by Staples Printers Rochester
Limited, Love Lane, Rochester, Kent.

ISBN 0 900102 756

Editor's Note

This book represents the collective wisdom of numerous people: those listed in Appendix ii, writers on the subject (listed in the Bibliography) and those with personal experience of this illness. Weaving together contributions from all these sources was my job and I have tried to do it without imposing my own style or approach. I have, however, made some editorial decisions. I have used the terminology: 'people with dementia' rather than 'people suffering from dementia' because I know that when handicapped or sick people voice a choice they opt for the former. The document also recognises that most people with dementia are in the older age groups although the principles of practice are the same for any age group. I have not specifically mentioned any settings except those providing day or 24 hour care. However, much of the document will apply to any setting. Finally, I have tried to confront the fact that different labels for departments and different law exists in England and Wales, Northern Ireland and Scotland by using all the labels/law in the text. Because of the differences in the law and its extreme complexity the legal section is only a very brief guide.

Editing this document has been a most rewarding experience because of the enthusiasm of the contributors. It is a totally collaborative document but I should nevertheless make it clear that, when differences of approach or views appeared, I made the final decision. Since this field is developing rapidly and we have found more and more enthusiasts, the document has become richer with each draft. Clearly this must not be a final, once and for all venture. An updated version will be essential within a couple of years. Nevertheless, we all believe that this book will help those struggling in this rapidly developing and challenging area of work.

Mary Marshall
Dementia Services Development Centre
October 1989

Contents

Chapter 1

Introduction

Why is this book necessary? Because people with dementia are a relatively new client group to many people working in the community. Most professional workers today will have to help people with dementia whereas it used to be a relative rarity. For most workers the disease well present new problems. The number of people with dementia is increasing very rapidly with the increasing proportion of people in their 80s and 90s. They are also a particularly vulnerable group whose position should be protected and enhanced. They are a group who present workers with difficult dilemmas such as the conflict between community care and residential care, between their needs and the needs of their carers, between rights and risks. These dilemmas are compounded by the shortage of resources and by lack of standard procedures which have been established in work with higher priority client groups such as children at risk of abuse. There is also a significant lack of skilled and trained workers in this field. Workers have therefore to rely on their own skills and judgement to a great extent with people with dementia and their carers.

What happened to people with dementia in the past? There were a lot fewer of them but presumably they were cared for by relatives and where this failed by admission to geriatric wards or psychiatric hospitals. Given that the numbers of hospital beds for older people have not increased proportionately, what happens now? Does 'community care' for this group have any meaning and what is the worker's role given the problems of separating out the psychiatric and social components of this illness? If community care means care by usually elderly and often female relatives, skilled workers are needed to organise provision of resources and support as well as to assist with the feelings of stress inevitably experienced by both parties. Workers will need appropriate guidance and training at both basic and advanced levels.

This book provides some guidelines as a benchmark for practice but they must not be so specific that they deny the unique individuality of each person concerned. Thus, although guidelines focus on the generalities, each situation will be unique. This is especially important to emphasise since this document mainly refers to old people with dementia and there is always a tendency to generalise about old people. Most of the document will apply to people with dementia at any age but since it is vastly more common in the older age groups this is the main focus of attention. Younger people have particular problems because the services, such as they are, are designed for older people and there is very little help indeed for younger people. They can also remain physically active and energetic which presents extra problems. The social dynamics can be very different too since they may be wage earners or caring for children. Some relatives can feel especially bitter about the occurrence of dementia in a younger person. There is also an emerging group of people with AIDS related dementia who present very special problems.

Guidelines are also needed because there are major issues of rights and risk involved. Guidelines should include ways in which workers can ensure that they are looking beyond the immediate concerns that can sometimes lead to removing a person's rights. They should also assist the worker so that the person with dementia receives the necessary support to help realise their own choices. The rights that people have which are threatened if they have dementia and which are of direct concern to workers, are usually the right to live with dignity, the choice of where to live and whether or not to accept outside help. Within certain economic constraints and with consideration for others in a community, these are rights that are valued by all adults. People with dementia, however, will find these rights threatened by the anxiety and fears of others, such as neighbours, police, relatives, doctors, nurses and social workers. Such threats can lead to a person's removal from their home against their wishes. People who are confused or have dementia are especially vulnerable to this because they may be considered to be unable to have a say in matters that affect their physical safety. Professional opinions can vary greatly on this issue: indeed in practice many people will have their rights undermined by professionals, especially when those professionals do not have any expertise in dementia. Anyone needing help cannot freely exercise choice unless real choice exists and they receive adequate information and support and unless they can be sure that their choice will not lead to their receiving an inferior service. Many people are afraid to choose for fear of upsetting the professionals. Since services for elderly people generally are rarely adequate it is only too easy for the rights of those with dementia to be undermined.

Guidelines, therefore, need to address the issue of rights and risk in a context of well informed practice. This document provides some basic information about dementia but is primarily concerned with working with those with dementia and their carers. It is intended to counter-balance the view that people with dementia do not need skilled care. To give an example from social work the 'common observation that elderly people receive social services while social work is reserved for the young' Booth (1987).

Many professions have published Codes of Ethics to provide basic principles of practice. For nurses, midwives and health visitors there are the following especially relevant sections in their *Code of Professional Conduct*: 'Act always in such a way as to promote and safeguard the well being and interests of patients/clients.

Have regard to the workload of and the pressures on professional colleagues and subordinates and take appropriate action if these are seen to be such as to constitute abuse of the individual practitioner and/or to jeopardise safe standards of practice.'

In the *Code of Ethics of Social Work* it states: Basic to the profession of social work is the recognition of the value and dignity of every human being, irrespective of origin, race, status, sex, sexual orientation, age, belief or contribution to society. The profession accepts a responsibility to encourage and facilitate the self-realisation of each individual person with due regard for the interest of others.'

The Occupational Therapists Board has issued a statement for industrial relations purposes. It includes: 'No registered Occupational Therapist should 1. By any act or omission do anything or cause anything to be done which he/she has reasonable grounds for believing is likely either to endanger or affect adversely in a substantial way the health or safety of a patient or patients.'

The Code of Conduct for Psychologists issued by the British Psychological Society includes the following sections: 'In all their work psychologists shall value integrity, impartiality and respect for persons and evidence and shall seek to establish the highest ethical standards in their work.'

Specifically they shall: 'recognise and uphold the rights of those whose capacity to give valid consent to interventions may be diminished including the young, the mentally handicapped, the elderly, those in care of an institution or detained under the provisions of the law; where interventions are offered to those in no position to give valid consent, after consulting with experienced professional colleagues, established who has legal authority to give consent and seek consent from that person or those persons.'

Chapter 2

Dementia

What is Dementia?

Two issues surround the use of terms like 'dementia'. First, practitioners must be clear what they mean and have precise definitions to carry into practice. Second, by whose authority is the definition to be made and against what norms is a definition of abnormal to be made? What meaning will the definition 'abnormal' carry? Presumably in a non-ageist society, which provides resources within the community to enable old people to achieve their choices, the meaning behind the definition will carry fewer negative overtones.

What is dementia? Dementia is a disease. It is a condition of brain failure and is more common in older people although it can occur at any age. Basically there are two main types of dementia: an overall deterioration of brain tissue (of which the main type is Alzheimer's Disease) and multi infarct dementia (a series of tiny strokes) which causes more erratic deterioration and is caused by faults in the blood supply to the brain. It is tempting but inappropriate, to delve too deeply here into the medical picture of dementia, but the following quotation from Murphy (1987) sets the scene very well: '*Dementia* is a frightening word. It conjures up pictures of wild-eyed people running amok, violent and deranged. Nothing could be further from the truth. Whilst it is true that dementia means 'loss of mind', in medical terminology it denotes a group of progressive diseases of the brain that slowly affect all the functions of the mind and lead to a deterioration in a person's ability to concentrate, remember and reason. Dementia can affect every area of human thinking, feeling and behaviour. The disease starts silently and very slowly so that it may have been progressing insidiously for two or three years before anyone notices anything seriously amiss . . .Dementia is the specific medical term that refers to a defined group of mental conditions, which can affect people of any age.'

Dementia passes through several stages as *Mrs C* illustrates: Mrs C is in her early eighties, lives alone but near to her son and daughter-in-law. She is physically very fit and walks several miles each day. Her memory is very poor and the two most common incidents are losing money and losing her door key. She spends a lot of time talking to the photograph of her daughter. She is very trusting of strangers. She likes her home and wishes to remain there. Her son respects this but worries about her safety and whether she is happy.

As the condition progresses she fails to recognise her son although she still walks to his house. She later begins to believe that he is her husband and as a consequence resents her daughter-in-law who is living with him. This has the effect of reducing the family's ability to support her.

Shortly after this time she wandered one night, fell and broke her leg. The injury required a long hospital admission during which she completely forgot about her own home. She was admitted to a nursing home and expressed no desire to leave.

Mrs C remained in the nursing home quite contentedly for just over a year until she died. She was able to appreciate having her son and daughter-in-law visit, although she never really knew who they were.

It is helpful to understand that dementia is a progressive disease along what might be described as a continuum. Some authors have seen it as a set of stages. Gwyther (1985), for example, sets out a list of behaviour in stages. This is an invaluable book in its clarity and is useful for all workers although it was written for nurses. Below is a list partly derived from Gwyther but presented as a continuum from onset phase through to the terminal phase:

Forgets what was just asked to do

Confusion about place – gets lost on way to shops

Shorter attention span

Problems recognising close family and friends

Repetitive statements

Makes up stories to fill-in blanks

May see or hear things that are not there

False memories

Poor judgement – makes bad decisions – problems organising thoughts – thinking logically

Trouble handling money – paying bills

Problems with reading, writing and numbers

Can't find right words

Perceptual – motor problems – trouble dressing

May have ideas, fixed or otherwise, that aren't real

Needs full-time supervision

Other presenting symptoms may include:

Loss of spontanaeity

Loss of initiative

Mood/personality changes

Anxiety about symptoms

Keeping to oneself, withdrawn

Difficulty making choices when more than one option

Takes longer with routine chores

Restless, especially in late afternoon and at night

May be suspicious, irritable, fidgety, tearful or silly

Loss of impulse control

Won't or can't bathe

Loses weight

Social disinhibition

Terminal Stage (may be complicated by institutional factors)

Can't recognise family or self in mirror

Loses weight even with good diet

Little capacity for self care

Can't communicate with words

May put everything in mouth or touch everything

Can't control bowel, bladder

May have difficulty with seizures, swallowing, skin can breakdown, infections

As you will be able to see from the list, as dementia progresses it affects a good deal more than memory. It is generally accepted that dementia involves a global loss of ability and that all areas of the brain cortex (or surface layer) will be affected. This layer of tissue is specialised and each part is linked to a group of abilities. The types of functioning that will be affected can be grouped as follows:

Memory
Language – comprehension and expression

Motor skills
Visual and perceptual abilities
Intellectual skills e.g. abstraction
Educational skills e.g. reading, writing, arithmetic

While a detailed assessment of the loss of these skills is not always necessary, it can be beneficial for some individuals to undergo assessment in order to, for example, find relative strengths. While there is a common pattern of loss for many, there are also many individual differences. If an individual loses, for instance, their relatively less deteriorated verbal comprehension, visual comprehension or reading ability might be stressed as better methods of communicating. Also, an individual who suffers from difficulties in controlling impulses will be likely to show not only a difficulty in waiting and perhaps inappropriate social behaviour, but may also repeat themselves, be unable to think out a solution to a problem, or have difficulty in deciding what to do in an emergency because all these abilities are coordinated within the same area of the brain.

For more detailed information on neuropsychology and the neuropsychological aspects of dementia, Walsh (1982) is helpful.

Intervention has to be based on an understanding of this continuum as well as the past experience, personality and present circumstances of the person with dementia.

Bannister (1978) reminds us of the distress felt by carers: 'The pain of dementia is felt not only by the patient/client, but by the carers. In an ideal world this would be minimised, though it will always be painful to watch a loved person lose their mind and personality, and behave in ways they would have deplored. Most of the problems of dealing with dementia come not from the failure of cognition, but from the behavioural consequences of this. Ideally these behaviours – wandering off and getting lost, leaving gas on, incontinence, inappropriate disposal of faeces – might be made less threatening to the peace of mind of the carer. Scrope Davies, in a letter written in about 1831 to Thomas Raikes said "Babylon in all its desolation is a sight not so awful as that of the human mind in ruins."'

Anton-Stephenes (1984) describes the clinical picture as a degeneration which affects 'within wide variations of time and intensity, the three major aspects of our existence – our intellect, our emotional feelings, and our behaviour. In each there is a characteristic loss or diminution of a previously existing function.'

The underlying physical diseases which give rise to dementia may on the whole be untreatable. However, it is necessary in each and every case for a full medical examination to take place, in order to ascertain whether the symptoms do in fact indicate dementia and that any other treatable illness is identified. Perhaps particularly poignant is the depression that can occur with people still retaining moments of

7

insight. Depression and dementia can occur at the same time at any stage Jacques provides useful information on depression in his book *Understanding Dementia* (1988).

Care must be taken to distinguish dementia from delirium (acute confusional state) which may be manifested in old people who are suffering ailments such as infections, high fever, drug reactions, bad diet, shock or constipation. These are acute conditions which demand immediate medical assessment and treatment. It is crucially important to differentiate between confusion and dementia, because confusion may be a symptom of both delerium and dementia. The key is speed of onset: delerium happens suddenly, dementia usually develops gradually. Taking a good history is therefore essential.

Sensory deprivation presents a labyrinth of problems which can further complicate and obscure the diagnostic process. Deafness can be isolating and predispose depressive illness. Poor hearing may prevent people from assimilating new information which can be misdiagnosed as short term memory loss or diminished comprehension Some people may try to conceal their deafness, whilst others pretend to be deaf in an effort to cover up their failing memory. Confabulation – the making up of stories in an attempt to conceal gaps in memory, may simply be misinterpretation of facts due to deafness. Paranoid thoughts may be the result of perfectly innocent, but misheard remarks. Failing eyesight can effect the accuracy of perception of surroundings which may induce or exacerbate an existing problem of disorientation. This can manifest as wandering or incontinence due to difficulties with locating, or recognising places. Altered auditory or visual perception can lead to misdiagnosis of hallucinations of audio or visual origins. Other disabilities can confuse the picture too such as severe immobility restricting social contacts. Good diagnosis and assessment should clarify aspects of any situation which are treatable or can be ameliorated. Dementia is often unrecognised by doctors, carers and workers in its early stages which is demonstrated by the enormous numbers of undiagnosed sufferers known to exist.

There must always be the question of 'whose problem is it?' because in some situations quite severe dementia is tolerated without difficulty. Conversely confusion caused by anxiety and stress may be in the mind of the carers while the person with dementia copes well.

Self-Determination and Dementia

A key issue for any worker is the application of the fundamental principle of self-determination: the rights of clients to decide for themselves and when a worker decides for clients. All workers will be familiar with the referral of an old person by a third party (relative, neighbour, professional) based on their concern which is usually accompanied with suggestions about what should be done (old people's home, day care, etc). When the worker visits and explains about the resources which can be provided, the old person declines all services. Is this resistance indicating personal (physical or mental) pathology or the exercising of a right? One thing is quite clear in both English, Northern Irish and Scottish law: unless the person with dementia is under some sort of legal order they have the *legal* right to decide for themselves. To whom should the worker ultimately turn? What action should be taken?

Workers are daily confronted with crises that include a plea to remove someone from their home. It is good practice to first work with the crisis, to reduce the level of stress so that the plea for removal can be reassessed by those making it. O'Hagan explores this in greater depth in his book, *Crisis Intervention In Social Services*, (1986). All professionals have a duty to help protect people from making decisions at a point in time when they are unable to give the matter their fullest consideration. This use of crisis intervention skills can protect self determination. In this field crisis intervention skills must include fullest co-operation with colleagues, who may feel themselves already full stretched. It is, of course, helpful if procedures have been worked out beforehand especially on matters such as confidentiality, the key worker (see Chapter 8) and access to resources.

Professionals usually place great store on client self-determination, not simply as a value position based on citizen's rights to determine the course of their lives, but also because much intervention can detract from self-determination: for example when so many referrals are not made by clients themselves. That said, no right is absolute and a balance has to be struck between the rights of the client, other members of the client's social system, and members of other systems (neighbours, community, professionals, society).

Mrs E demonstrates how careful support in spite of risks enables Mrs E to remain for a long period at home which it is known is where she wishes to be. (In this case the GP knew Mrs E well enough to make this judgement).

Mrs E lives alone in a large house. She was referred by the cottage hospital after being treated for burns to her legs caused by sitting too close to the electric fire. The GP was reluctant to refer earlier as he thought it would result in admission to the psychiatric hospital. This had been his experience in the past.

Mrs E believes that her parents and husband are upstairs and that she is looking after them. She has irregular eating and sleeping patterns. A programme of home support alleviates a lot of the risks and the electric fire is removed and replaced with a convector heater. This helps but she takes to sitting with her legs on top of the new heater and continues to burn them.

Visitors to the house are greeted as long lost relatives.

A relative is appointed Receiver and her bills are paid to avoid loss of any servies.

Over a period of a year she regresses and now thinks she is a young girl. She forgets how to dress herself sometimes and will eat things such as hand cream. She has reached a stage where she no longer recognises her own home and is beyond the ability of the community services available. She is moved via hospital to a private residential home. She still thinks she is in her own home with her parents looking after her.

There has to be a balance between rights and risks. A person always has the right to take risks but they have an equal right to be protected if their judgement is impaired. These are very major issues with this client group and they need to be aired and reviewed constantly with colleagues.

The King's Fund have produced a challenging report *Living Well into Old Age* (1986), which presents a set of principles for people providing services for those with dementia. Although these seem self evident, they are well worth careful scrutiny and are therefore quoted in full below.

Key Principles

This paper is about practical change in services but we believe that improvements can only be achieved by continually reviewing the principles held by people with a stake in changing servies.

The principles of our existing services are very muddled. They are a mixture of government statements, the traditions of the past and day-to-day solutions to problems drawn up by staff. Much of the policy is unwritten. What is certain is that all policies involve some basic beliefs and values about the nature of mental disability and about the place of elderly people in society.

Principle 1

People with dementia have the same human value as anyone else irrespective of their degree of disability or dependence.

People who do not work and people who have serious disabilities risk being undervalued in our society. Women, too, are often undervalued. Since many people with dementia fall into all three categories, they are at risk on all three counts. Expectations about quality of life for people with dementia must not be allowed to fall below the standards of other members of the community. Services should be concerned not just with meeting minimum standards but with positively demonstrating the value and importance of older people and people with dementia.

Principle 2
People with dementia have the same varied human needs as anyone else.

This means not only basic needs for food, warmth, shelter and protection from physical hurt, but also for affection, companionship and opportunities to take part in worthwhile activities. They are entitled to share in the whole range of life's experiences as other citizens do, alongside other citizens in the mainstream of society. Only when they live as others do can people with dementia be accepted as having equal value. Only by living as others do will they have access to the same range of human contacts and resources. What we are aiming for here is not simply living in the community, in the sense of living outside a residential home or hospital or being cared for by the community without access to proper help from professionals and services: as we see it, real 'community care' implies being cared for as a member of the community. To achieve that objective for people with severe dementia and to help them to enjoy some of the benefits of community life will require a high level of long term support, professional skill, imagination and resources.

Principle 3
People with dementia have the same rights as other citizens.

People with dementia are often denied their rights and the opportunities and resources to which they also have a right. In many cases, they are unable to assert their just demands on their own behalf. Where people with dementia do not themselves have the ability to claim their rights, it is the duty of those who serve them to find alternative means to claim on their behalf and to preserve their rights jealously. When formal steps are taken to change the legal status of an individual the safeguards and access to representation should be the highest standard expected by other citizens.

Principle 4
Every person with dementia is an individual.

People with dementia, like anyone else, have the right to behave as individuals, within the limits of the law, and to be seen as individuals with their own preferences, abilities and needs.

One part of individuality is being helped in ways that are personally tailored to you. A second part is making sure that your individual history and past life are not lost and forgotten by those around you. Individuality means having continuity between your past, your present and your future.

11

Principle 5

People with dementia have the right to forms of support which don't exploit family and friends.

It is the informal support of families, friends and neighbours which provides the major proportion of help for people with dementia. These carers have the right to expect a normal quality of life, without being exposed to stress and exhaustion. Those providing services have a duty to ensure that they actively recognise and support the work carried out by carers.

There are situations in which the needs and wishes of the elderly person conflict with those of the carers. Services should be concerned that both parties' rights are safeguarded.

Chapter 3

Context: Social

General

The proportion of elderly people with dementia is greater in the older age groups. It is thought that up to the age of 80 about one in ten has this illness to a moderate or severe extent. Thereafter the proportion rises to about one in four or five. However these figures are by no means certain and a great deal of research is ongoing at present to assess these estimates and to examine the possibility that they may be higher or lower in certain geographical areas. Given the ageing of the pensioner population (due to the ageing of the baby bulge who survived infancy at the turn of the century as well as increased life expectancy), the numbers of people with dementia are increasing very rapidly at present. Given too the drop in the birthrate between the wars this is a generation with relatively few sons and daughters to care for them. Many of this generation never married. About 25% of todays pensioners for example have no children at all, let alone having children living locally. These figures have been spelt out for Scotland with their policy implications by *Scottish Action on Dementia* (1986) who point out that 81,000 of the probable 91,000 people with dementia live in the community.

Thus we have a dramatic increase in the very old age groups (by as much as 81% of the 85+ group between 1981 – 2011 for example) leading to an increase in the number of people with dementia. This places considerable burdens on a system which artificially separates health and welfare responsibilities into two bureaucratic monoliths. In Northern Ireland an integrated health and social services structure at least offers the possibility of a more coordinated approach. For the rest of the United KIngdom this organisational mismatch is exacerbated by other trends such as the continuing high priority being given to children in need by social work/service departments and primary health care and to acute services by health authorities. The severe limitations in finance available for health and welfare services, the increasing role of an uncoordinated private and voluntary sector and the move towards less institutional care for psychiatric patients also

13

contribute. The government policy context in more specific terms is admirably spelt out in Norman's book *Severe Dementia: The Provision of Long Stay Care* (1987).

Some of the problems of providing properly planned and coordinated community care were spelled out in Sir Roy Griffiths' report *Community Care: An Agenda for Action*. At the time of writing the details of the White Paper based on this report were not available although it is clear that local authorities are to have a key role. For people with dementia whose needs combine health and social aspects, there may still be major problems in integrating the two kinds of services.

Old people with dementia and their carers are as disadvantaged as other older people in our society. They share with their contemporaries general trends such as the older you get the more likely you are to be alone, badly housed and poor. (See Chapter 6.)

Social Model of Disability

The social model of disability as described by Oliver (1983) can also be applied to people with dementia. This model involves viewing the disabilities of individuals, not solely as a result of the impairment with which they are afflicted, but as a consequence of the failure of society to plan and accommodate people who are not able bodied and minded. Society caters for illnesses through health services which are aimed at curing and returning people to their normal state. However when a condition does not respond to treatment and becomes chronic, the individual is treated as having special needs that at an extreme, will mean their segregation from the rest of the community. We do not design our world to accommodate people who are chronically ill.

In this way we see people with dementia for their inabilities and usually fail to take account of their abilities. Society's expectation is long term residential or nursing care, not that the person should be enabled to live as before with special planning to lessen their disabilities. While many relatives will continue to care because of the strong emotional attachments that exist, they will often find themselves isolated from their friends, impoverished by their non-productivity and having to fight the local authority bureaucracies in order to get help. People with dementia and their carers will find themselves being directed towards special groups that are separate from their previous world.

For those working with people with dementia and their carers, it is important to analyse and assess their problems from this perspective as it recognises that individuals are not necessarily personally at fault for their failures. It can be very supportive to help people to realise this, so as to avoid some of the deep feelings of frustration that can occur if they are left to feel that they are responsible for their situation. It will also lead workers to value the importance of intervention on a community level rather than solely the individual level.

14

Mrs Q lived alone in one of a row of council bungalows. There was no warden, and no-one took any care of her. She showed many of the signs of dementia, in that to the alarm of neighbours, she left unlit gas taps on. She would defecate in inappropriate places, and then make half-hearted attempts to hide what she had done, and she would wander the streets bizarrely dressed, and forget where she lived. She first came to my notice when I went to investigate an argument just outside my house. It seemed she had taken exception to an allegation made by a pyrancantha bush. I offered to walk her home, and she immediately forgot the bush and began to tell me that her brother in Australia was just about to send her £50,000.

We have improved since the days when Mrs Q would have been burnt as a witch, but what might be an ideal way of coping with her? She was regarded with a mixture of fear and derision by most of the neighbourhood, children and adults alike. It would have helped her a great deal if there had been more informed understanding; then other people would have been prepared to help her find her way back home rather than jeering at her when she got into disputes with bushes.

Rural Areas
Rural areas deserve a special mention because most models of care, training and practice are based on assumptions more appropriate to urban than to rural life. Rural areas are usually neglected in documents like this. But there are special problems in rural areas.

In sparsely populated rural areas, institutional resources are often far distant from people's homes thus making it very difficult for a resident to maintain close ties with their own community.

There is a need to provide social stimulation to people who are otherwise deprived of it by their isolation. Although day centres may do this effectively in urban areas, the trauma of long bus rides to distant towns may outweigh the benefits gained. A minibus journey can be used as a reminiscence session if properly staffed but this is not always the case. There is a need to develop small locally-based resources or have visiting schemes which provide for the person's needs without the trauma of travel.

Stigmatisation can be more prevalent in some rural areas as there is less opportunity to be amongst varying social groups, due to the smallness and closeness of village communities. This may give rise to a reluctance to report new problems at an early stage which may result in crisis intervention rather than planned care. Isolation itself can mean that the condition is not noticed in its early stages. The development of locally based services which can gain the trust of members of the community is essential. In many remote areas of Scotland the efficacy of small scale dispersed residential and day care units alongside other resources has been well proven.

In areas where neighbours, family and friends do rally round they tend not to make contact with official services until the situation reaches a level of desperation. If there are local services, commonly known to people and readily accessible, families and others make contact with these at an earlier stage and work in cooperation with them. If help is available locally preventive work is very rewarding because in many small communities, there can be enormous tolerance of behaviour in someone who has been well known and much liked in the past.

Chapter 4

Context: Legislation

This section is relevant primarily for social workers although it is important for other workers to understand the law and its limitations.

Sadly, the British legal system disregards the problems of people with dementia. Any legislation that is used by social workers and others in an attempt to cope with the problems caused by dementia was originally designed for use with other client groups. In desperation, pieces of legislation have been seized upon and used, often inappropriately, in an attempt to protect the rights of this most vulnerable client group. 'During the slow process of the disease, sufferers gradually lose the abilities needed for rational decision making. These include communication by, and understanding of, speech and writing, mathematical calculation, perception of risks, memory of recent events and decisions, recognition of people and places, intelligence and reasoning, motivation and drive, emotional responses, and judgement and conscience.' (Scottish Action on Dementia, 1988.) As a result, they may put themselves in physical danger by wandering, failing to eat properly, refusing medical treatment or leaving a gas cooker turned on. They may neglect personal hygiene and make irresponsible decisions about finances. In addition, the person with dementia may become unduly suggestible and therefore susceptible to all types of abuse by relatives, professionals and others.

The dilemma for professionals is obvious. How can a client's right to self-determination be balanced against an equal right to be protected when unable to make rational decisions? There are several possible approaches:

1)   The client's right to self-determination is paramount.
Mrs Brown is neglecting herself at home, wandering at night and is very lonely and unhappy. She refuses to contemplate life in a residential home. She is at risk. Everyone, except Mrs Brown, agrees that 'something must be done'. But what?

17

The social worker can, with Pilate like precision, wash her hands of the whole business. "Well I tried. She won't sign the forms for residential care. What more can I do?" The most likely outcome from such inaction is that the supporters will all keep their fingers crossed that nothing dreadful will befall Mrs Brown before the G.P. has prevailed upon a hospital consultant to admit her to long-term hospital care. At least no papers have to be signed for that.

2) 'Work in the best interest of the client'–social worker or 'Act in good faith' – doctor

Both these positions have some credence in legal circles. However, both are open to abuse.

The unfortunate Mrs Brown now has a new social worker who smiles at her constantly, appears kind and whom Mrs Brown 'sort of' recognises and trusts.

As any competent professional knows, it can be very easy to make things happen *to* the Mrs Brown's of this world. A smile here, a reassuring pat on the arm there and lo and behold, Mrs Brown is 'snug and safe' in residential care. The professional can sleep easily at night, knowing that she has done her best for her client.

Alternatively, a doctor can ensure her admission to hospital 'for assessment' and equally ensure that she never returns home again.

Can either professional be blamed for these actions? Is this approach any better or worse than the laissez-faire attitude of the first worker? The third alternative is recourse to the law.

3) Adapt existing legislation.

How many people with dementia have had to leave their homes because they had not managed to pay their bills? This can be the first sign for professionals that things are going wrong.

Miss Fraser, now retired, had been a dressmaker. Her sister, Emily, who had died three years previously, had always kept house for them both, paying bills and doing all the cooking and cleaning. When the professionals first became involved, initial thoughts were that Miss Fraser was severely demented. The house was in a mess. Kitchen assessments by the occupational therapist showed that Miss Fraser could scarcely make a cup of tea, never mind the cheese on toast. The social worker had to liaise with the district council and the electricity board because of massive unpaid bills. Miss Fraser was just not coping and something would have to be done.

Fortunately for Miss Fraser, the staff nurse in the day hospital noticed that Miss Fraser had a rich inner life and that her short-term memroy was better than that of other patients in the reality orientation group. The truth was that these housewifely skills had only recently been learnt by Miss Fraser – Emily had always coped – and therefore, in the dementing process, they were amongst the first skills to be lost. How could the law here help delay her admission to residential care?

Protection of finances
1) Power of Attorney
This gives one person power to act on another person's behalf in all financial matters. It is intended that the attorney shall carry out the directions or wishes of the sufferer because he or she is physically incapable of acting on their own behalf. As dementia is a progressive illness, there comes a time when the sufferer can no longer give valid directions so that, theoretically, this piece of legislation then becomes invalid. Nevertheless, these written mandates are often acted upon long after incapacity has deprived them of any legal effect.

2) Enduring Power of Attorney (does not apply in Scotland)
Since March 1986, it has been possible for a person who feels he is becoming less able to run his affairs efficiently to create a Power which can continue in the event of subsequent mental incapacity. If the attorney, under an Enduring Power, has reason to believe that the donor is, or is becoming, mentally incapable she/he must apply to the Court of Protection to register the Enduring Power of Attorney. Before making this application, the attorney must notify the donor and that person's closest relatives of the application. Once the Enduring Power of Attorney is registered, the Court of Protection has the power to give directions on the management of the property and affairs of the donor, the rendering of accounts and the keeping of records, about which the Court can require information. It can also cancel the Power if the attorney is considered unsuitable, and will hold a hearing at the time of registration if objections are made by those notified.

3) Court of Protection (England and Wales) Office of Care and Protection (N. Ireland)
The Court is part of the Public Trust Office and is responsible for the financial affairs of people suffering from mental disorder and carries out its duties by appointing a receiver who is usually the nearest relative or a solicitor chosen by the relative. The Court may not consider a receiver is necessary when a person's needs are being met and he or she has few assets; and if needs are not being met but assets are less than £5,000 the Court may be able to make a 'summary order' and no receiver need by appointed. Application to the Court can be made through a solicitor or by personal application to the Court which will give an applicant assistance in completing the necessary forms. The application must be supported by a medical form signed by a doctor.

The receiver will be appointed after a hearing, and will have to account each year to the Court for his/her management of the estate. The Court charges an annual fee based on the annual income of the incapable person, and not on the work done, and an advantage of the Enduring Power of Attorney has been seen to be the avoidance of this extra drain on a person's resources.

4) Curator Bonis (Scotland)

In effect, a financial manager is appointed, following a petition to the Court of Session in Edinburgh or to a local sheriff court. Unfortunately, this is a very costly business as a solicitor or accountant is usually appointed curator as accounts are scrutinised annually by the Accountant of Court. The Accountant of Court does not usually recommend curatorships for estates under £15,000 because of the fees involved. For smaller estates some Regional Councils will direct their own legal departments to carry out this function and bear the cost themselves. If however the sufferer eventually goes into local authority residential care there arises the question of one local authority department having the power to pay another department the costs this involves from the person's estate.

5) Appointeeship

An appointee is a person appointed by the Secretary of State to act on behalf of a DSS claimant who is unble to manage his own affairs. The appointee must apply in writing to receive the money due to the beneficiary and social security staff are instructed to satisfy themselves as to the beneficiary's inability to manage his/her affairs, usually by means of a doctor's letter and a visit by an officer of the DSS to the beneficiary who will also wish to see the appointee to confirm their suitability. The benefit remains in the name of the beneficiary but the appointee signs for it and uses it in the interest of the beneficiary. Sums involved can be considerable as those persons requiring an appointee will usually be in receipt of the Attendance Allowance, and some will be in private residential or nursing homes where they are funded by Income Support. Elderly appointees have been alarmed at the sums of money they carry regularly away from the Post Office, but Income Support cannot be paid directly into a bank account, nor is it thought desirable that the proprietors of a private home should be the appointees for their residents.

Protection of the Person – Welfare

In Scotland, when a mentally disordered person requires to be treated in hospital either for his own health or safety or to protect others, he can be detained in hospital for up to 6 months as a result of proceedings before a sheriff. Detention can be continued for a further 6 months, and thereafter for periods of a year, on medical reports. On these occasions there is no court hearing but the patient can appeal to the sheriff on each renewal of detention. In an emergency, there can be detention of up to 72 hours on the recommendation of one doctor, and for a further 28 days on a psychiatrist's report, without any judicial proceedings. Evidence suggests that the number of people with dementia detained under these powers is relatively small. This is not because there are few sufferers who would satisfy the legislation, but that doctors and mental health officers prefer to remove their patients on a 'voluntary basis', and usually succeed in doing so.

In England and Wales, similar legislation is available. 'From a lawyer's point of view the problem with this approach is that most of these "voluntary" patients are probably incapable in law of giving legal consent to removal or indeed to treatment.' (Ibid.)

Guardianship has its origins in the 'boarding out' of mentally handicapped people with unrelated guardians. A guardian's powers are limited to deciding where his charge shall live, making him attend for treatment, occupation, education or training, and ensuring access to him by a doctor, mental health officer, or other such persons. The guardian is given no powers to consent to medical treatment or make decisions about financial matters.

The National Assistance Act (1948) Section 47 and the 1951 amendment allows the removal of someone suffering from 'grave chronic disease', or who is old, infirm or physically handicapped and living in insanitary conditions. This applies in England, Wales and Scotland. The equivalent in N. Ireland is Article 37 and Schedule b of the Health and Personal Social Services (N.I.) Order 1972. Removal can only be ordered if the person is unable to look after themselves properly and no one else is doing so. He can be detained in hospital or other place, e.g. a residential home, for up to 3 months although this can be reviewed for further 3 month periods.

Dementia is sometimes defined as a 'grave chronic disease'. However, arguments continue as to whether this ageist legislation should remain on the Statute Book, or whether it should be retained with many more safeguards for the individual. This legislation does not apply to a young person, however insanitary and objectionable to other people their living arrangements may be, and it is felt that the public health legislation should be used in both cases. In some part of the country the Section is never used and in others the medical officer of health feels it serves a purpose; but the crux of the argument is that the Section removes the liberty of a person who is capable of making valid judgements about his situation. The proposed amendments are all to enable the person to have every opportunity to return home once their home environment has been ameliorated, after having benefited from a period in whatever was considered a 'suitable place', so that the loss of liberty should be as brief as possible.

The Way Forward: The Need for Reform

When the Disabled Persons Act (1986) is fully implemented it will lay on local authorities a duty to provide a written assessment of need and provide the disabled person with a right to representation whenever their case is discussed at planning reviews. This should be helpful, but is not enough.

In 1986, Age Concern England published *The Law and Vulnerable Elderly People* in which they made definite recommendations. Their definition of vulnerability would include those suffering from dementia, and they recommended that local authorities should have a general power to promote the welfare of old people and a new duty to consider and assess the needs of a vulnerable elderly person and/or the carer of that person at the request of that elderly person, or the carer, or another person who was shown to have a proper interest. Written reasons for the subsequent plan of action would have to be given and Age Concern England proposed an Intervention Order enabling individual old people and/or their carers to oppose or to appeal against a decision of the local authority and to enable a local authority to oppose or appeal against the decision of an individual. An Emergency Intervention Order would enable direct application to be made to a court (ideally a family court if that were introduced in this country) in a situation of immediate grave risk, and a judge could make this order for a maximum period of seven days. It could direct that specific help be brought to the old person where she/he resides, subject to the availability of such help; or that the old person be removed to a place of safety; or that named individuals be restrained from assaulting, molesting or otherwise interfering with the old person or be excluded from the old person's home. Age Concern England emphasises full consultation and regular reviews through the procedures.

Scottish Action on Dementia have proposed some basic principles on which new procedures should be based. Firstly, that every person who is by law incompetent, or approaching incompetence, should have a legal right to comprehensive care and protection. And secondly that any compulsory intervention in the life of such a person should respect his dignity as a human being and be the minimum necessary to provide sufficient care and protection.

In their document *Dementia and the Law* they continue by describing a system of Mental Health Panels, based on the Children's Hearing System. This system would involve thorough assessment, reviews, take into account the needs of carers and be administered by lay people through a Reporter. This would take the process out of the formal court setting which anyone who has been to court with an elderly person with dementia will agree would be an improvement.

The way ahead is not easy. As professionals we can work uncomfortably and sometimes illegally doing our best for clients but acting outside the legal system in a way which would not be tolerated for other client groups. We can attempt to adapt the present legal systems to protect people with dementia or we can campaign hard, for reform.

Existing Legislation

England and Wales
Guardianship: 1983 Mental Health Act
Court of Protection: 1983 Mental Health Act
Removal powers: Section 47, National Assistance Act 1948 &
                National Assistance Amendment Acts
                & Public Health Act 1936
Chronically Sick and Disabled Persons Act 1970
Disabled Persons (Services, Consultation & Representation) Act 1986

Scotland
Guardianship: Mental Health (Scotland) Act 1984
Curator Bonis   Judicial Factors Acts
Removal Powers: Section 47, National Assistance Act 1948 &
                Section 83 1896 Public Health Act
Chronically Sick and Disabled Persons Act 1970
Disabled Persons (Services, Consultation & Representation) Act 1986

Northern Ireland
Guardianship: The Mental Health (Northern Ireland)
                Order 1986
Court of Protection: The Mental Health (Northern Ireland)
                Order 1986
Protection of Property   The Health and Personal Social
                Services (Northern Ireland) Order 1972.
                Schedule (b)
Removal powers: The Health and Personal Social Services
                (Northern Ireland) Order 1972.
                Schedule (b)
Chronically Sick & Disabled Persons (Northern Ireland) Act 1978

Chapter 5

Context: Professional, Inter-professional and Multi-Agency

In many agencies and professions there is an increasing movement towards client group specialisation. There is evidence that some agencies are giving elderly people a very high priority, nevertheless, the picture is, on the whole, a gloomy one. For example, staff allocated to work with elderly people in general and people with dementia in particular are often untrained because in many settings this field of work is not considered deserving of the highest quality of professional attention. Neither is there sufficient training for such work, both on basic courses and on post qualifying courses in this complex and challenging field of work. This area should be given a very high priority for training budgets so that staff in teams in the community, in residential and day care settings, in hospitals and management are trained to understand the problems and to acquire the necessary skills. The availability of joint funding (support funding is approximately the same in Scotland) money has meant that many voluntary organisations are providing essential services, often without sufficiently experienced staff, adequate professional back-up and availability of good training. On the other hand some specialised agencies such as Alzheimer's Disease Society/Alzheimer's Scotland have contact people available who are highly knowledgeable and can be used to help other professionals to understand the disease.

Resources are a key issue for workers not only in terms of resources within their own agencies but also the availability and access to other agencies' resources. There is a need to avoid assuming responsibility without the provision of adequate resources. This means that the responsibility must be shared with other professionals and their resources. Hence a need to be clear about professional practice in relation to that of other professional groups, and the need for very close co-operation. It is impossible to assist this client group without working jointly with other professionals and carers.

Within their own agencies staff may encounter indifference, hostility, apathy and apprehension: a variety of negative feelings about working with older people generally including people with dementia. Within such an atmosphere it is difficult to work creatively. Workers specialising in or interested in working with old people may believe that their colleagues view their work as of lesser importance than child abuse for example. Indeed workers with all age groups may hold this view and the fact that it is also shared by management is illustrated by many agency priorities and allocation of resources. An important prerequisite to effectiveness, therefore, is to open up discussion about work with old people both generally and in respect of any particular project. This discussion can be included as part of training programmes for all staff. It ought also to be a regular item for meetings at all levels and in all settings in departments. It is important to raise the awareness and status of this area of work.

Even where attitudes of colleagues are supportive, resources may be inadquate. It follows that an important part of good practice with and on behalf of older people is campaigning with other agencies in order to achieve a more favourable and more varied allocation of resources. Consumers and consumer groups may usefully be recruited as allies in such work. Scottish Action on Dementia has this role and a similar campaign is emerging in England led by Alzheimer's Disease Society.

Professionals work in teams or networks of different sorts both within their own agencies and with people from other agencies. A team or network, within an agency such as a social services/work department could be social worker, occupational therapist, home help organiser, volunteer organiser in a local office or a staff team in a residential home. Interagency community teams or networks might include all or some of the following professionals: psychogeriatrician, geriatrician, social worker, community psychiatric nurse, district nurse, clinical psychologist, general practitioner, occupational therapist, physiotherapist, speech therapist, chiropodist, audiologist. Locally based dementia teams combining hospital and community personnel are beginning to emerge. The combinations vary but the issues of interdisciplinary work remain.

Even when the idea of multi-disciplinary assessment and service delivery are accepted the implementation of care on a team basis can often prove difficult to achieve without some tension between the professions.

Each agency and profession has its own view point based on training and experience. A successful team makes full use of these differing views to achieve a comprehensive assessment and service for the elderly person. The individuals involved share in mutual respect and a tolerance of differing philosophies. They feel a great deal of support and help from their colleagues. There is a feeling of trust rather than one of suspicion and threat typical of poor team work.

Workers cannot work with people with dementia in isolation from other professionals whatever their discipline. Good practice is infinitely easier if one's colleagues are of a like mind. One of the skills needed in this field is the ability to work jointly with colleagues from other professions. Techniques for dealing with hostility or indifference are not easy to acquire but may be learned. Individual members of a smoothly working team can disagree during discussions about a plan but once implemented it is important that each member of the team accepts responsibility for it. Similarly, members have to tolerate overlap, an issue clearly demonstrated by Murphy in *Dementia and Mental Illness in the Old* (1986) in which she describes the work of a psychogeriatrician. With only tiny modification this could be a description of almost any worker's role such is the extent of overlap.

When people are working as part of a team with professionals from other systems, each professional must renegotiate with this new team the theories, authority and status which they hold in their original settings. To import into interdisciplinary work simply the authority and roles held in their original setting may result in ineffectiveness and/or conflict. For example, doctors are often given (and might expect) higher status than other team members which may be at odds with levels of experience. All other professional involved have to recognise experience as well as basic skills and knowledge in their colleagues. Doctors are used to clinical responsibility and to decision-making but another team member may have greater knowledge of the resources available. It is essential, therefore, that the participants clarify the roles they will play and how decisions will be made. A report by the British Psychological Society's Division of Clinical Psychology entitled *Responsibility Issues in Clinical Psychology and Multi-disciplinary Team Work,* (1986) well clarifies terminology, implications and the issues involved in multi-agency work.

The primary health care team can have a crucial role in the early identification of dementia. Since in each general practice there may be only a small number of patients with dementia, there may not be enough opportunity to develop the necessary skills. Health visitors and district nurses need to be alert to gradual changes in abilities and personalities. They should have easy and quick contact with professionals who can provide advice, diagnosis and support, for example, community psychiatric nurses and clinical psychologists.

There is considerable potential conflict between GPs and social workers in spite of the shared problem of lack of resources. This can be exacerbated if the GP is on call 24-hours seven days a week, and is a sitting duck in the surgery. The social workers have many more defensive strategies. The role of the health visitor, the district nurse and the community psychiatric nurse may need clarification both with colleagues and with clients. Most important is the realisation that the roles, responsibilities and resources of all those involved will overlap and without close collaboration will cause muddle and conflict. All workers need to appreciate which skills are shared with each other and which skills are specific to certain members of the team.

Many teams and networks fail to involve the key people. Typically ignored are the home-helps and the carers/relatives. These groups of people probably know the elderly person better than anyone else; they are the key communicators with the elderly person and it is they who will implement most of the plans and have to respond to most of the crises that occur.

The other important person who is usually omitted from the discussions is the elderly person themselves. This is particularly true when the elderly person has a diagnosis of dementia. The team must remember that although the confused elderly person may be misperceiving their environment, they are still deserving of at least basic human rights, dignity and respect. These rights include freedom of choice. Elderly people with dementia, like all of us, experience a full range of emotions and should be involved as much as possible in plans and decisions about themselves. If the elderly person for whatever reasons, cannot really be fully involved, care should be taken to involve a true advocate. This is not necessarily a professional or relative who may have needs of their own which conflict with the needs of the elderly person. It is also important to ensure that 'team decisions' are clearly communicated to the elderly person rather than presented as a fait accompli.

There is a need for the very highest standards of professional practice in this work given the possibilities for bad practice. Depending, for example, upon the doctors and social workers involved, a person may be removed from their own home by coercion, they may be left there without support because policies only keep them out of an institution but do not cover the provision of alternative services, or they can receive positive help towards living their life as they wish.

Age Concern England's Working Party on multi-disciplinary approaches to the care of elderly people within the community entitled *Working Together* (1988) addresses many of the issues involved. The research group found very little evaluated work on multi-disciplinary teams although quite a lot of descriptions of good teams existed. The group looking at multi-disciplinary approaches in practice addressed good examples as well as potential pitfalls and reached conclusions directly related to implication for training at all levels. Unfortunately good examples of multi-disciplinary training are few and far between. There are occasional courses run by one profession and open to another but shared ventures are rare. Perhaps an increase in joint training ventures will not simply strengthen the knowledge base but more importantly enhance the building of good relationships and a mutual understanding between all the agencies involved.

Effective teams or networks are essential to really effective work with individuals. They assist planning, minimise duplication, identify key workers, improve knowledge and skills and provide mutual support. They have considerable potential too in the wider spheres of interdepartmental planning or exerting concerted tactical pressure on separate agencies to achieve the same ends.

Chapter 6

Context: Financial

The financial context has several negative characteristics:

Coping with dementia is an expensive business.
It is expensive for carers who may need to pay for extra help, equipment, respite or sitting help, replacements of furniture, bedding and other household items, and replacement clothing including shoes and slippers in situations of incontinence, extra heating if their relative is at home and for fares for visiting if their relative is not. Too often residential units (local authority, private, voluntary and health authority/board) are inaccessible rather than placed in local communities. There can also be costs of care of children or other relatives because the relative with dementia sometimes needs undivided attention during hospital visits.

The initiative to claim extra help always rests with the carer or the person with dementia.
Almost no financial assistance is given automatically. The initiative to claim any benefit or allowance rests with the carer or the person with dementia which is clearly unsatisfactory. There are numerous reasons why people do not claim: they may not understand or be aware of their entitlement, the forms or the system. They may not wish to associate themselves with the poor and have to submit to a means test (although benefits such as invalid care allowance and attendance allowance are not means tested). They may have strong feelings about privacy or be frightened of officialdom. They may simply be too weary.

Claiming financial assistance is complex and people can be woefully ignorant or misinformed (including professionals).
Claiming financial assistance is not easy. Criteria of eligibility are often difficult to understand; some which discriminate on the basis of age seem inexplicable. Forms are often very complicated. Some claims require written verification from doctors, others require a subsequent

visit from a doctor. Even people with dementia and their carers who are in touch with professionals do not always get the advice they need given the serious lack of knowledge of GPs, nurses and social workers. Some clients will simply need information and explanation; others will need help and support. Some will need help to see themselves as carers entitled to financial help. Many will need advocacy especially in dealing with appeals which are often required. Workers should arm themselves with the *Disability Rights Handbook*. Books written for older people include Age Concern's *Your Rights* and for carers the Carer's National Association's *Help at Hand*.

Even once the person with dementia is in residential or nursing home care the difficulties do not stop. Relatives may need to ensure that the resident/patient is getting their personal allowance (the amount specified for personal items) and they themselves may need help with fares. They would also be advised to calculate the money available to pay the charges over several years to ensure the money does not run out. The R family organised a Curator Bonis (the Scottish alternative to the Court of Protection) to handle their mother's finances when she went into private care. The solicitor did not notify the family of the financial crisis until a debt of £700 had arisen from the home and their mother was on the point of eviction. The family could not afford to continue to pay the fees and a place had to be found for their mother in a local hospital.

People with dementia and their carers will need help to cope with a system that is both baffling and humiliating. Sustaining the claimant's self esteem whilst assisting them can be very important if they are not to give up. Carers' groups can play an invaluable role in this although there will usually be a need for individual discussion and support.

Note: A list of useful organisations is in *Appendix iii*.

Chapter 7

Context: Race and Culture

The literature which exists on elderly people from black and ethnic minorities in Britain is slender. The subject of mental illness among ethnic minorities has a significant literature, none of it, however is on black and ethnic minority elderly people.

For the majority of black and ethnic elderly people Britain is a second or third home rather than the country of their birth. Their expectations of old age have been shaped in Africa, West Indies, India, Pakistan and Bangladesh where both life style and status of elderly people are very different from that in Britain. Many who are now elderly have not worked long enough to be eligible for a pension and are dependent on social security. In their working lives they experienced disadvantage and discrimination in the job market often doing most menial jobs and night shift jobs. Linguistic problems sometimes meant that they failed to avail themselves of medical and welfare provision. The worsening economic situation often hit them hardest.

Many of the problems facing black and ethnic elderly are similar to the UK European elderly; such as poor housing, low income, social isolation, poor health and impaired mobility. In addition to these the black and minority ethnic elderly face stigma and prejudice of racism as well as ageism.

Although different family dynamics and life style exist in different countries such as West Indies, India, Pakistan, Bangladesh and Africa, they share a common attitude towards elderly people. Elderly people by and large are shown respect and they tend to have a position of authority within the household. With change in family patterns in this country, elderly people find themselves increasingly left alone and without a status role in the family and in society.

The loss of familiar kinship support, loss of dignity in the society, loss of long cherished dreams such as the dream of retiring home but not being able to do it and the experience of unfulfilled ambition make the black elderly more vulnerable to physical and mental illness. The DHSS study of service delivery of minority ethnic groups in the North West (Hughes and Bhaduri, 1987) showed that the onset of stroke and dementia was common amongst the Afro Caribbean elderly people who were relatively young (late 50s or early 60s). There is an urgent need for research in this field.

The need to make a proper assessment is essential for service delivery. Cultural sensitivity should illuminate and not obscure common human needs. It must not perpetuate assumptions about different life style which will lead to inadequate assessment and inappropriate service delivery.

There are implications for those caring for black elderly people whose short term memory becomes affected. Workers need to listen and learn from their black clients in order to understand the milieu where they were brought up, their religious beliefs and the cultural factors which fashioned their early development. If carers have no understanding or knowledge of the elderly person's racial experiences and cultural background, they will find it difficult to establish a rapport with clients talking about their past. It is necessary to try to understand the attitude and expectations carried over from their younger days. For example, an Indian elderly woman resented the care she was receiving from her daughter-in-law, which however good, did not compare, in her eyes, with the way in which she had cared for her own mother-in-law.

Society's attitude to normality varies from culture to culture. For instance, an elderly person meditating under a tree may be seen as normal behaviour befitting a devout in India, whereas it may be seen as a sign of dementia in Britain. Such cultural differences may often lead to wrong assessment or the wrong approach which may reinforce confusion in the process of dementia for a black elderly person. Aggressive and paranoid behaviour may be fuelled by wrong assessment and wrong treatment.

All kinds of assumptions are being made by policy makers, managers and practitioners about black and minority ethnic elderly. For instance they may wrongly assume that Asian families will always care for their ageing dependants or they are most likely to go 'home' (to their country of origin) after retirement. This failure in understanding is compounded by the black and minority elderly not pressing for a better retirement here and putting up with deprivation and loneliness while dreaming of a return home. Many statutory and voluntary agencies have regarded the low referral rate from black and Asian elderly people as an indicator that their families are providing sufficient care or that they are unwilling to accept help. This myth fortunately is being gradually dispelled. Even if their families are willing and able to look after their elderly relatives they may need domiciliary and day care support. Some of the ethnic elderly people in this country with no next of kin are greatly at risk. Because ethnic elderly people may be widely dispersed and are not numerous, there can be a temptation for the service givers to dismiss their needs. Whatever elderly people in general suffer in this society black elderly people suffer more. Policy makers need to know what black and ethnic minority elderly people want in order to meet their needs as the existing services are geared to meet the needs of native elderly people.

Workers should ensure that both the carers of black and ethnic elderly people and the elderly people themselves are aware of service provision. Access to information and benefits is generally dependent on the person's ability to read and speak English as well as make sense of what are often complicated regulations and explanations of them. Many elderly people including the Chinese, Cypriots, Vietnamese experience difficulty in using services because of language problems.

Workers need to have knowledge of the values and the network of support systems of the communties. Assessments should be made in the context of this knowledge.

Staff with the relevant experience, language and knowledge should be deployed. An information gathering exericse of the communities should be undertaken.

Specialist workers need to be appointed. Specialist not only in the particular field of specialism i.e. elderly, mental health, but also in their knowledge of cultural and racial issues.

Many improvements in the quality of life for black and ethnic elderly people may not require major changes in the service delivery, but may be achieved by relatively simple modification to existing services and by using imagination, and willingness.

The pratitioner must be trained to communicate with black and ethnic elderly. An example from social work is given in an article by Bhaduri (1988): R Phipps, Care Group Coordinator for Moss Side Afro Caribbean group for elderly and infirm people said, 'social workers do not seem to communicate well with Afro Caribbean elderly. For instance, one elderly lady was left to fill in a form by a social worker – the social worker did not even know that she was illiterate.'

Managers should employ trained interpreters. Practitioners should be trained as well so that they can properly use interpreters for making assessment and care plans.

It will be useful to identify needs as defined by elderly people and then to consider various ways of meeting them. This will warrant innovation in offering a range of services for black and ethnic minority elderly people with dementia. The range of services should include appropriate and sensitive day care and domiciliary services, residential care, translated literature, interpreters and trained staff.

When dealing with dementia it is important to bear in mind the likely losses experienced by the elderly person. These are as follows:

1) *Loss of income* – It leads to loss of authority and status. It is particularly painful for the black elderly who come from a community where being elderly is associated with prestige. Even their own family members may be seen to have failed to offer support as they have to

move away for better jobs, leaving the older generation isolated and vulnerable.

2) There is a *loss of opportunities* for all elderly people, but is felt to a great degree by black elderly people.

3) *Loss of respect*, is often shown when elderly people are patronised. Ageing is seen as negative and problematic.

4) *Added losses experienced by black elderly people.* Added stress can be brought about by racism, by growing old in a society where one feels unwanted.

5) *Loss of long cherished dreams* or the non-fulfilment of ambitions. Many who have dreamed of returning to their homeland are unble to do it.

6) *Loss of familiar kinship support.*

7) *Deprivation* – isolation, poverty, loneliness and the need to cope with what may be a hostile environment.

8) *Loss of following bereavement* – the older one becomes the chances of outliving relatives and friends are greater. It is necessary for workers to understand how the individual reacted to loss in previous experiences and how culture differs in grief reactions.

The workers should try to prevent further stresses. One should remember the importance of rituals which may make an elderly person feel secure and comfortable, especially if the person is suffering from dementia.

Chapter 8

Skills

Communication: Verbal/Non-Verbal

With the interdisciplinary team

Interdisciplinary teams do not necessarily work together as an integrated team unless effort is put into doing this, and much overlap of visiting and conflicting plans can arise. The significance of a 'key worker' as a contact person within this group is extremely important.

The term 'key worker' is used in this book in two ways. In the day care or residential setting it means a supervised care assistant who acts as confidante, advocate, counsellor, practical helper and record keeper for an individual member/resident. They usually get to know the person with dementia and their family very well. A parallel role can exist in community care although it may not involve so much personal care. It may involve more coordination and progress chasing. This person is identified by the multidisciplinary team to act as the link person between the family and the practitioners involved. Sometimes in this context the relative can be the key worker.

A team can only function to the benefit of the client if each member knows and respects the expertise of the others. Exactly the same applies to teams or networks in different departments and organisations covered in the chapter 5. Recognising that working with other professionals is a skill that must be learned is half the battle. The other half has to do with knowing and understanding their language, approach, knowledge, values and systems of accountability. A problem often arises over the important area of diagnosis and assessment. It is important to share an understanding of what is meant by diagnosis and assessment and that this should lead to an explicit, preferably written *plan* including decisions about who will implement it. This plan should be made with the client and the carers and they should have a copy of the written version. Communication with all these different people is very easily wrecked by unspoken issues like status, power, attitudes, professional isolation and accountability.

With the client with dementia

Communication with a person with dementia requires at the outset an understanding of the level of comprehension retained by the client. We should not immediately assume that the client is incapable of any choice or of expressing any opinion. The advice of a clinical psychologist and a speech therapist is invaluable. Like other clients the person with dementia has the right to be informed of decisions taken on their behalf. Workers must make sure that they can be heard and seen, that the client understands the language being used, and that all the usual skills of communication are being used. Communication must also include non-verbal communication. Leaving crucial information in written form may also be helpful.

Both the carer and the person with dementia may be fearful of change, for different reasons. An overtly warm, accepting, concerned, compassionate approach is essential, where possible openly demonstrating affection. The use of touch, taking the old persons's hand while sitting with them, not standing over them, may well help to build trust. Where words and meanings no longer hold their value people are quick to sense in an intuitive way when they are cherished and wanted, or when they are seen as a nuisance.

Communication with a person with dementia will depend on an assessment of the effects of the dementia on the individual at that time. In the early stages when a person still has insight there can be a lot of anger, anxiety and depression. They can appear to be paranoid when in fact what they are doing is covering up for diminishing competence. Sometimes in trying to cover up failings, a person can make themselves even more confused.

Mrs B, when asked her age by the consultant psychiatrist, got very angry and replied – "I tell no man my age." which could have been true, but in fact she could not remember how old she was.

The worker has to be realistic and has to help the person express frightening and distressing possibilities. Confronting with questions like "Have you been having trouble with your memory?" can be helpful. Comments like "People think I'm daft." demonstrate how distressing this experience can be. Many people know only too well what is going to happen and as a consequence may become depressed. They need an opportunity to cry as much as they may need practical help like memory aids.

A sufferer quoted in *The Loss of Self* (Cohen & Eisdorfer 1988) described his feelings as follows: "Every few months I sense that another piece of me is missing. I can only think half thoughts now. Some day I may wake up and not think at all. Not know who I am. We all expect to die some day but whoever expected to lose themselves first?"

36

As the dementia progresses workers may have to continually say who they are. At this stage friends and even family may withdraw and the workers have to try and get people to stay in touch. Carers can become very isolated if they live with the person with dementia. Sometimes if the person is behaving oddly the worker should ask them what they are doing. Their response may indicate that they think they are somewhere else, for example, at work. When this is explained to carers and friends the behaviour can seem less peculiar and less frightening. A person with dementia is still acting rationally in their terms. The secret of understanding this is to tap into what that rationale is. This underlines the importance of obtaining a good life history initially.

Nurses in a day hospital found one lady very difficult to cope with because she made personal comments about their appearance and kept asking them what they thought they were doing. When it was explained that she had herself been a ward sister and that she was 'managing them' it made their lives a little easier.

Workers often have to intervene when the client is distressed. The technique is to explain things very carefully and try and hook it to something s/he does remember. A reassuring manner can be a great help. It can also be a good idea to give them the idea that they have worked it out for themselves, for example: 'remember when you came in this morning, we put your coat onto a hook'. It can be less stressful not to ask open ended questions, although asking leading questions can force people to agree to wrong things. Sudden stubborness can be a problem: "No, I'm not going to have a bath." After a short time try: "Let's get you a good wash with your feet in the bath." – a certain face saving element is thus introduced.

Workers may need to advise someone with a failing memory how to cope. Writing things down, putting notes in diaries and keeping written personal histories and photographs can be very helpful. This can be especially helpful if there are a lot of paid and unpaid carers involved. In a sense, if they are able to be sufficiently involved, the worker can become the 'keeper of the memory'. Memory loss is a very complex problem. It is usually variable, inconsistent, partial and rarely total. People with dementia can often remember certain people and things they had previously forgotten. It also seems as if, with some people at least, minimal ability to learn, for example, places and people is retained. Communication might be enhanced by realisation of the possibility that the client's long term memory might be much better than memory of recent events. The more a worker knows about a person with dementia's past and family, the better. Then by regular reference to people, places and events which were of significance to the person, the worker can often 'bring them to life' and thus facilitate discussion about current problems or plans.

Insight may not be completely lost until the disease is very advanced but it is easy to miss the evidence because it can be given allegorically rather than directly. It may be necessary to read 'clues'. Interpretation is much easier if you have knowledge of the person's past life.

There is considerable debate about the best way to handle mistaken identities or situations. The client, for example, thinks her mother is alive. Do you accept this as her reality and include mother in conversations – or not? Do you agree to disagree? Probably each situation should be considered on its own, bearing in mind the effect the mistaken identiy has on the present circumstances, the degree of agitation of the client, their strength of feeling and the intransigence of their convictions. Setting people right for the peace of mind of the carer is seldom justified. Confrontation should be avoided at all costs and every effort made to read and respond to the underlying emotions and the mood of the communication even if it is not possible to decipher the actual verbal content. Practical help should always be given with tact. For example, with reading and writing you might say "Shall I read that for you because the light is not too good?"

There is sometimes a psychiatric disorder overlying the dementia such as depression or paranoid illness and these need to be checked out. However, it is a common experience of workers in this field that apparently fanciful stories are in fact reality or have some basis in reality.

Mr H, aged 72, was admitted to hospital with Parkinson's and a drug induced confusional state. He kept talking about his concern for his mother. The ward staff assumed he meant his wife and asked the social worker to do a home visit. Mrs H was being looked after but Mr H would not be reassured. Mr H was gently reminded of his mother's likely age to no avail. It subsequently transpired that his mother was fit and well, aged 93. He was accustomed to doing her shopping for her.

Physical problems such as chest infections or faecal impaction can also cause apparent deterioration in a patient. The appropriate investigations should be carried out if there are any sudden changes of behaviour in order to exclude any underlying cause. Treatment should be given as necessary.

In the terminal stage another set of dilemmas emerge such as the extent to which the people should be controlled by drugs. Aggression in particular can be difficult to cope with and much effort may be needed to determine what is making the client angry. Often it is help with intimate matters which is very difficult to deal with. At this stage helping the carers is the highest priority.

When *Mrs S* hit his wife, she retaliated by punching him. She was profoundly shocked by her own behaviour knowing that her husband was in the terminal stages of dementia. She spent many hours huddled alone in the bedroom wrapped in a duvet and only spoke about it months later in a group.

There can also be problems with sexual behaviour. For example, some men may become very demanding, or some wives may find it difficult to respond to the 'changed person'. Many people with dementia become disinhibited in speech and behaviour which relatives find very difficult.

When verbal communication is limited or no longer possible there are principles of practice which in general should be applied. Touch is usually an important means of communication. It is important to observe the client's reactions, to where and how they are living and to the help they are receiving from others. Ultimately if the person is happy and demonstrates a familiarity with their environment, it should be taken as good enough reason to help enable them to continue living there providing they are not a danger to themselves and to others.

People with dementia may be fearful of receiving help from agencies as this may be seen as the beginning of a process which will ultimately remove them from their home. It is necessary to pay attention to the reactions to receiving help so as to develop the level of help in accordance with the level of trust that exists. Rejection of help should never be seen as a final decision. It may be necessary for another member of the team to offer the help or for it to be offered in another way at another time.

With Carers
Carers include relatives, neighbours, volunteers and friends who have a day by day caring relationship with the person with dementia. Much of the material in this section may also however be relevant for 'paid carers': workers in the caring professions such as GPs, home helps, community nurses, wardens in sheltered housing and other community based residential staff. It is fundamentally important that help for carers is available when it is needed rather than when they have struggled on to a crisis situation and reached a stage where help becomes irrelevant.

Carers need to be aware of the phases of dementia. The help they need and, will accept, will change as the illness progresses. At first professionals often regard relatives as co-workers. Gradually, over time, this can change and they may become clients. Carers can get very angry with memory loss thinking that 'mother is doing it on purpose to annoy'. The worker may have to explain and provide information about the illness as well as ensuring that a proper diagnosis is obtained Relatives will often deny the illness or feel very guilty that they have been angry in the past. The nature of the relationship between the carer and the person with dementia is all important in coping and making sensible plans. In some relationships the prognosis may result in the relative 'wrapping the sufferer in cotton wool' which has the effect of almost hurrying them along the road. Some relatives block off the news. Others plunge into caring with such overwhelming vigour they exhaust themselves. Role change is never easy but some cope much better than others. Carers whose relationships have been characterised by independence adjust more easily than those who are very dependent.

Mrs M first became known to the hospital team following a referral by her GP. to the psychogeriatrician. Following his first visit he requested that the social worker and occupational therapist visit the family at home. Mrs M lived with her son who worked some distance from home and therefore was away from home all day and her daughter who had learning difficulties. When the social worker and occupational therapist visited they found that Mrs M's son had placed many large notices around the house with which, together with prompts from her daughter, Mrs M was able to cope.

The social worker met the son on many occasions to offer support and advice. Mrs M's son was anxious to care for his mother and his main problem was her personal hygiene which he felt unable to supervise. Arrangements were made for Mrs M to attend a local elderly persons' home once each week for her to mix with others of her age group and to have a bath. After some time it was discovered that Mrs M no longer understood the notices she was reading and was therefore a danger in the kitchen. At this stage she was brought to the day hospital for three weeks for assessment.

Following the assessment Mrs M attended the elderly persons' home three days each week and rotating care was arranged to enable her son to go on holiday. The occupational therapist gave the family advice on how to offer the right prompts when Mrs M was dressing and encouraged them to keep Mrs M active at home by dusting, washing up. Mrs M became anxious some time later about her deceased parents. She did not always recognise her son and daughter. The elderly persons' home was finding it increasingly difficult to manage her. She was re-assessed at the day hospital and medication prescribed which settled the situation again.

As time passed her son found he was unable to leave his mother for the time after he went to work and before he came home at night. She did not recognise her family at all. Her son agreed to his mother moving full time into the elderly persons' home and visited regularly and took her home for day visits.

The elderly persons' home began to find it difficult to manage Mrs M when she became doubly incontinent. Following a case conference between her son, the social workers representives of the hospital and the elderly persons's home she was admitted to a continuing care bed where she died three and a half years after the first referral.

Factors which influence acceptance of help include the length of time the carer has been managing alone because this can lead to feelings of: (a) guilt if they feel they have 'given in' and accepted help; (b) anger that help was not around when it was needed earlier; and (c) grief reactions combing with guilt and anger. This is usefully spelled out in Gilleard's *Living with Dementia* (1984).

For some carers there is a prevailing sense of loss in the moderate and severe stages. They feel that coping with their relative is 'a living death' because the person they knew is no longer there with them. This mourning period is often lengthy.

Carers care for many reasons, not all of them straightforward. Relationships often have a long and complex history: sometimes longer than marriage as Pulling (1987) points out. Workers must try to understand the nature of the interactions and interdependence if communication is to be clear and help given appropriately. Caring for a person with dementia may also reactivate earlier unresolved family conflicts which surface around the issue of who shares the burden of care. In some situations professionals are well placed as honest brokers to convene family meetings designed to achieve reasonably acceptable caring arrangements.

In working with people with dementia and their carers it is most unlikely that 'perfect' outcomes will be possible. Part of skilled practice is for workers to accept, and be able to help others accept pain, loss and actions or plans which are only 'slightly better' or 'less worse'. They need to be able to support others as well as to sustain their own continuing warm concern and involvement.

Communication with carers is mainly about supporting them in their caring and should be a process of helping them to review their situation including risk factors that may be emerging or changing; providing information both of a factual nature and on management techniques. Sometimes the communication may be on behalf of the carer. Thus the worker may be conveying to others the pre-morbid personality of the person with dementia. This is absolutely vital for workers who have not known the sufferer's interests and lifestyle before the onset of the disease and particularly relevant if the worker is also going to organise respite care or day care as a relief for relatives.

The adjustments carers have to make are usefully described by Jacques in Age Concern Scotland's book: *Reaching Out to Dementia Sufferers and Their Carers* (1986). He summarises these as the lost relationship, the new relationship, the changing relationship and intruders in the relationship. He points out, for example, that changes in the person with dementia are never static: needs and personality change all the time. Families need to be warned that this may happen if they are to cope with it and all workers should be ready to modify their plans.

Part of the process of communicating with carers is legitimising their need for help. It is not simply helping them to work out what they need and organising it into a sensible package, it is working through resistance to help and the implicit feelings of failure they may experience in doing this. Help is often rejected if it is inappropriate, not good enough, comes at the wrong time, is given in a careless fashion or does not allow the carer some control. Communicating about receiving help is a very subtle skill. The danger in doing it badly is that carers give up caring because they feel diminished or they reject help and are needlessly exhausted andd overwhelmed by caring.

There is a need to help carers to see their own needs as carers, not simply in terms of the needs of the person for whom they care. Carers groups can help to do this, especially if they are not illness orientated but accept carers, regardless of the disability of the person for whom they care. Such groups will enable them to speak more freely about the realities of their tasks and their needs for help. Interviewing carers in the home of their dependent relative puts the focus on that person and will discourage people from considering themselves. Inconsiderate people would probably not be caring. Groups will also allow people to realise the extent of their stress, as many people first attending such groups are unaware of how many of their symptoms are related to their caring tasks. Groups will help carers not to suffer quietly.

Assessment

All professions see assessment as one of the key skills. There is a common core for each to assess as well as a specialist aspect. The common core which all professionals are looking at includes the person's background and family history, previous level of functioning and standards, problems perceived by the individual, the carer and the assessor, competence in activities of daily living and communication, carer's attitude to caring, carer's needs, health and social support. This section will deal with general issues rather than look at the areas that each profession is assessing although a general list of questions to help the whole team make a plan is included at the end of the section. The key questions in assessment are: who? where? why? how? when?

Assessment should never be made solely on the basis of a one-off visit. Neither should assessment be followed by an automatic programme of intervention. Nor should it be a once and forever assessment but, together with the resources provided, it should be monitored, evaluated and reviewed. The situation for both the client and carer changes all the time as do their needs. Workers need to be aware that gathering information about people from third parties without their knowledge is suspect, even unethical. It is important to be clear who is the client. Where interests conflict it may be necessary to have separate workers for the people involved.

Mrs K, a carer, made a plea at a conference for professionals to get together on assessment as she was sick of giving the same story to four different workers and her mother was bewildered by all the different faces and questions.

Assessment must be considered as the first and most essential task of any intervention. It is a judgement based on information gleaned from numerous sources about a person's problems and will determine the need for further intervention, referral and treatment. A comprehensive assessment is usually multi-professional and should involve the carers as well as the person with dementia.

A medical assessment is imperative to either confirm the diagnosis of dementia or identify the differential treatable condition which may present 'dementia like' symptoms.

Workers should ensure that they assess the cause of problems, whether these are to do with the people involved or the surrounding social situation. They then decide whether they fall within the ability of professionals to deal with, need joint work of some sort or need further referral.

Resources available may not always be sufficient to meet the needs but this should not prevent or alter the assessment. It may be necessary to accept the limitations of resources in the short term, but the assessment of needs will become evidence for those who advocate for more resources in the long term. Clarifying whether a problem arises from impairment, disability or handicap will determine the 'target' of intervention. It may determine the need to gain better medical care; to give support and care for the client; to support the carers or to help them adjust attitudes; and to challenge the inadequacies of resources. The range of targets is endless but if they are not identified by assessment, intervention can become ineffective and self indulgent.

Assessment will result in identifying existing support and the need for a care programme. Programmes should be structured so as to ensure that the needs of clients are being met and to give adequate support to families and other carers who are also involved. It is good practice in supporting carers to help them to provide the care they wish to provide and to relieve them of other burdens.

The major difficulty with assessment is that it must be carried out to a particular standard or it will lack credibility. This has implications for training and practice. Workers need to be able to make firm recommendations as to how assessment is carried out. Labels stick for ever. The need is for multidisciplinary assessment, including an assessment of the environment in its broadest sense including attitudes of neighbours, proximity of hazards like motorways and the environment as perceived by the client. Assessment goes on constantly. Every person with dementia should have a right to a multi-disciplinary assessment which will, if necessary, include in-patient or day hospital assessment, resulting in a written care plan with built-in review dates and identification of a key worker. No client should be admitted to a residential or nursing home without a full assessment and an allocation meeting attended by the residential staff (who should have visited the client at home or in hospital), the key worker, relatives and other involved parties.

Assessment should always be objective and not influenced by expectations. Assessment can be skewed when a relative/carer expects a worker to arrange for an old person to be removed from the community and the "client" expresses a differing view. The worker may want to emphasise the authority of the client to make choices and decisions whereas the client and the carer may see the worker as having authority as a consequence of the agency in which they work, their knowledge and expertise. The worker needs to be clear what is happening, which may mean seeing this situation as the carer 'evicting' the client, or the carer needing to safeguard their own or their family's health and well being. One of the purposes of assessment should be to assess the ability of the carer to continue to cope.

In making an assessment it is important that workers define their terms very carefully e.g. terms like 'depression' can be used very loosely. Another related problem is to be aware that the diagnosis 'dementia' often blinds us to other needs which should also be assessed such as deafness.

It is important to examine the positive in assessment, i.e. *what the client can still do* rather than what has failed. There is a real danger that worker, client and family can get caught up in a downard spiral unless some attempt is made to identify areas which may enable people to think positively. There are in fact even in the grimmest situations often some examples of continuing good functioning, even though they may not be areas which other people are seeing as particularly significant at that time.

The following sequence is helpful in considering how to approach assessment:

1) Are they aware that the referral has been made and on what terms?

2) What is the problem/situation? How is it perceived by those involved?

3) Who is it a problem for?

4) Why is it a problem now? Why referral now?

5) Why is help being sought now?

6) What solutions have been tried and with what effect?

7) What changes are those involved looking for?

8) What changes would they settle for?

9) How will you know if these changes have been achieved?

10) If successful, may the changes make something else worse?

11) Who is going to do what, including being key worker? And by what date?

12) How is action/change going to be communicated to others (including clients and carers?)

A clear written statement about what is to be offered should be shared with the client, formal and informal carers. This can be helpful as a means of integrating the varied services. It is also important that any arrangement should be regularly reviewed. Situations can change very radically, particularly after effective intervention and a date fixed to do this at an early stage can give people a goal to work towards.

Since April 1987, the Disabled Persons Act 1986, has required that local authorities always take into account the ability of the carer to continue to provide care, whenever they are assessing the needs of a disabled person. This includes people with dementia.

The Act also extended the duty of local authorities to provide people with information about services that are relevant to their needs, from services provided by the authority to services known to the authority. It is most important for local authority employees to ensure that they are fully informed about such services if they are to fulfil their legal obligations.

Assessment of resources available in terms of location, quality, access, etc. is not wholly straightforward. Many workers do not know the full range of resources available outside their departments. This is where a local 'dementia team' which includes voluntary organisations and the private sector can be invaluable. Ideally lists should be readily accessible to professionals and the general public. Carers in particular often have no idea what is available. It is not just a matter of knowing what and where. Quality can vary vastly and can change rapidly as personnel change. Willingness and ability to help people with dementia depends crucially on the people offering the service who, in turn can be much more generous and flexible if properly supported. Organising the various elements of a care package demands great skill and such packages require regular review. It is only too easy to provide a person with dementia and their carer with a service such as a visitor, or day care or special gas taps, only to find that the helper's tolerance does not extend to the more difficult behaviour or to the deteriorating condition. This is complicated by the fact that many people with dementia can deteriorate sharply with a change in circumstances and only improve again as they settle down.

Staying Client Centred

Staying client centred is not easy in this world of short term solutions, exhausted carers and general low priority of this client group in any setting. The first step is to work out who or what is the 'client'. Where do we focus our efforts? Thinking of our work as being in a set of systems can be helpful.

It can be helpful to use systems thinking in both analysing the component parts of any situation and in working out where to direct the effort. The classification of systems is usually in terms of client, action, target and change agent. These can be explained as follows:

1) Client system: those requesting help or engaging worker's services.

2) Action system: those with whom practitioners need to deal and secure secondary agreements in order to accomplish tasks and achieve objectives.

3) Target system: may be the client system but comprises those the practitioner needs to change or influence in order to accomplish the objectives.

4) Change-agent system: helper whose purpose is bringing about planned change.

The most useful decision is what is to be the target system because the use of this kind of language frees the worker from the assumption that they necessarily have to change or influence the client or family. In some cases the target system may be another professional worker or may be a consultant or may even be the worker's own departmental/agency policy.

It is important to be realistic about what can be changed and to make sensible judgements on what is short term, medium term and long term. These are not mutually exclusive of course. Too often attempts to change unhelpful policies are abandoned because the worker is faced with very urgent and immediate needs. Identifying and dealing with target systems in the medium/long term like departmental or hospital policies are nearly always best done by a group of people – a dementia team, a BASE (British Assocation for Service to the Elderly) group or some other joint forum.

Increasingly departmental policy is the provision of short term input only: a highly specific service or package of services and then no further action.

Professionals need to help sustain family carers through the long haul of their relative's illness. The 'hit and run' approach of unconfident, unskilled, warring and under resourced professionals of whatever discipline is entirely inappropriate to sustaining old people and their carers who face the ravages of an extended and intensive dementing illness.

Workers involved in planning care need to be experienced in the likely outcome of their planning. The care of a person with dementia is long term (probably longer than much child care work) and the needs will change considerably. Planners need to take this into consideration and not to view this work as needing only short term intervention. There can often be conflict between departmental policy on closing cases, case loads and workers who are trying to provide a continuing service. Mr and Mrs A illustrate the length of time a worker may need to be actively involved.

Mr and Mrs A are both in their 70s. Mr A has Parkinson's Disease and Mrs A has dementia (Alzheimer's type). They were referred because Mr A was falling and Mrs A was calling the neighbours or police to help lift him, usually morning or evening. The GP was requesting admission to residential care as the only solution. Friends and neighbours were agreeing with the GP as they are fearful of consequences.

Neither Mr nor Mrs A want to leave home and they are wary of accepting any help in case it leads to admission. Mr A could be better if he took his medication regularly but Mrs A forgets this.

Mrs A still cooks and looks after the home, lunch is often before breakfast. She is beginning to have difficulty coping with the results of Mr A's incontinence.

Eventually home help is accepted on a daily basis and this is sufficient to prevent the situation from deteriorating. A few months later Mr A dies. Mrs A has difficulty in remembering that he has died and needs reminding. Each time it is as if she is being told for the first time. A new neighbour is very supportive. Mrs A does not know how to pay her bills or do her shopping. She still manages to cook and clean the house. She is vulnerable as she will invite strangers into the house. This causes extra concern to her carers.

After a further few months she begins to wander in the late afternoon. She is looking for her husband. When she cannot find him she rings her home help. Her conversation is now very repetitive and she has difficulty recognising close friends. She often thinks that her home is elsewhere though when it is explained to her that she is in her own home she affirms that she wishes to remain. The GP no longer visits because of her dementia but has accepted the role of the social services department in co-ordinating her care.

After a while Mrs A's home help leaves and is replaced by someone with less skill in communication. She feels responsible for Mrs A and is concerned by the risks. She and the neighbour campaign for Mrs A's removal. A distant relative has become involved and appointed a friend to oversee her. This friend often is found shouting at her for forgetting things. Mrs A becomes quite frightened and begins to withdraw and does not trust anyone. The social worker tries to get her to the day hospital where she would be amongst understanding people but she has lost her trust in him.

He arranges for the home help to be changed and increased so as to take over the work of the neighbour and a person with greater skill is recruited. Mrs A soon responds to the change and trusts the home help enough to allow her to take her to the day hospital. Once there, she is overjoyed at having so many people to talk with that she becomes sad when she has to leave. This was interpreted as a request to leave home and she was admitted for a trial stay to a nursing home. After a short while she was very settled and showed no desire to return home.

Much intervention is in short term bursts of effort but will result in re-referral as the situation changes. It is not necessary to continually monitor a stable situation (professional workers' time is too valuable) if adequate systems of re-referral can be achieved. Clients and carers must be given the knowledge of how to refer and workers must ensure they respond to requests.

This is not the same as offering a crisis service because it implies first that there is a plan, second that there is a key worker and third that there is a system of regular view. The point is that the worker does not necessarily have to do all of these. The plan is drawn up by a team of people which should include the carer and should have identified a key worker, who might most usefully be the home help or community psychiatric nurse. A card with the key worker's name, address and telephone number in large clear type should be left with the old person and also with their principal carer.

This use of the term 'key worker' is not unlike the role of 'case manager' which is a term increasingly used. A case manager organises resources to form an individually tailored package of care. The idea that there is a team backing up the case manager is not always accepted whereas it is assumed in the concept of key worker. Increasingly it seems that a case manager will have sole responsibility for mobilising and organising the 'package' of care for the client. This may work for one type of care such as day to day assistance in basic activities of daily living. It is unlikely to work if the full range of assistance which includes health services, housing, recreational and spiritual matters are included. There is also the possibility of the worker feeling torn between the roles of rationing services and being the advocate of the person with dementia and their carer.

People unable to advocate on behalf of themselves will need and deserve others to do this for them. Workers will have to act as advocates in those areas of need which come within their professional expertise. Advocacy will only be credible if it is preceded by an assessment of actual need, rather than need relative to departmental policy and resources. Workers must maintain a professional independence from resource rationing in order to act as advocates.

Workers need also the establish an independence of medical protocol if they are to be effective advocates for medical services. Acting on behalf of clients in relation to the private sector is a relatively new area and one which needs more attention. The use of written agreements may clarify expectations on both sides.

It can be useful for the worker to see themselves in a negotiating position on behalf of the client in relation to others. Much of the management and trade union literature about negotiating procedures can be very helpful especially in the planning stages. What is it we would like for our client, what would we accept and what must we have? The aim is to get the best deal for clients without alienating other people and professionals around them. Workers are trying here to help a group often wholly unable to express their needs, let alone understand how they can be met.

One way in which workers can attempt to maintain a balance between conflicting needs and enhanced self-determination is through the use of working agreements: contracts with the person with dementia and their carers and with caring systems involved. The latter does not, of course, mean a contract with another person/agency on behalf of the person with dementia. No one has the right to give consent on another person's behalf. Three things, however, can be seen to invalidate any agreement made: duress, undue influence and incapacity.

Types of working agreements and those pressures which might invalidate them are examined in greater detail for social workers in Corden & Preston-Shoot (1987). Much of their thinking is relevant for other professionals entering into agreements with clients. They stress the importance of participants in a contract understanding that they have entered an agreement and that there are therefore shared expectations of all parties. They also remind us that workers can be powerful people from the point of view of clients and that care must be taken not to dominate; rather that the client's needs and wishes are central, not the agency's and that if the agreement is not entirely in line with the client's wishes they fully understand the reasons for this. It is this last point which is the crucial issue with people with dementia. Is it ethical to make contracts with a client with dementia? Given that dementia is a process; who decides what a person can decide for themselves and at what stage they become incapable of deciding? Corden and Preston-Shoot argue that, if social workers wish to defend themselves against accusations that the contracts they negotiate in some contexts are void because of the client's incapacity, they need to show that the contracts are appropriate to the conditions and requirements of the 'incapable' party. A more honest and more ethical model may be to use the legal process of guardianship. It is also important to work, as the guardian, on the basis of seeking to establish what the person is likely to have wanted had they not been impaired. This can involve a lot of work but is the best basis for determining the wishes of the client.

Respite care can be a lifeline for carers and yet it is often provided on a spasmodic basis rather than on the basis of an agreed contract. If carers know exactly what to expect and when, their stresses are enormously diminished. They will also sometimes test out a contract to ensure it is real. If, for example, they have been promised admission if the situation becomes intolerable they may request it and then when arrangements are made as agreed, they may change their minds. They will however make fewer demands thereafter because they know they can trust the contract.

If contracts are a way of being quite clear with those with dementia and their carers about what all parties have agreed to do, they only work when there is agreement in the first place between carer and cared for. Often there are very difficult conflicts.

Conflicts of interest that exist between carers and clients can be lessened by early and appropriate support. However, this can turn to bitterness if they are left unsupported. Support to carers is generaly too little, provides more help and encouragement to male carers compared with female carers and often consists of occasional, rather than regular relief. Regular daily or weekly support with the caring tasks that are found most oppressive by the carer can reduce the conflict, but a constant review is always necessary.

This is a field of work which is a minefield of conflicts of interest: painful, personal and often unresolvable conflicts of interest. The most painful is usually that between the relative and the person with dementia. Meeting the needs of one can mean denying the needs of the other. As with any other conflict of interest the answer is a properly negotiated compromise where the best possible outcome is achieved for both parties. This may need separate representation for each party and workers should avoid getting themselves in a position of being the sole arbiter in the middle. Conflicts of interest can occur between the patient and the hospital, the client and the community, the person with dementia and the other residents of a home and so on. There is always the risk that if conflicts of interest are not taken seriously they can result in total breakdown in relationships and much guilt and unhappiness. It must, of course, be recognised that there are seldom 'perfect' solutions but there is often a 'best possible' solution.

Sometimes the conflict is not reconcilable. It is necessary here to support carers who wish to withdraw their care. It is also necessary to protect the interests of the client. This becomes hazardous when client and carer share a home. This difficulty demonstrates the need for preventative work and the error of a social poilicy which encourages care in the community without adequate funds.

Mr D was in his mid 70s and had dementia. He lived with his wife, son and daughter-in-law. In the past he had been cruel to his wife and for this reason was not easily tolerated now he was vulnerable. He remembered very little of what occurred daily but was not distressed by this. He used to go out alone to the pub but had no road sense. He walked slowly up the middle of the road. He often urinated up against the back door. He was sometimes aggressive towards his wife. This always occurred when his son was out and his wife was trying to get him to bed.

The family refused any help in the home and would only accept help that removed Mr D. As a consequence he attended day care. While at the day centre he spent most of the day with a woman who he thought was his wife. His family found this amusing and were not upset by it.

The family coped well for some time, partially out of loyalty to Mrs D and partly because Mr D had a high level of pension upon which they relied. The frequency of respite care increased and when Mrs D became ill, Mr D became a permanent resident in the local psychogeriatric hospital. He was familiar with this place as he attended for day care. He became physically more frail and beyond the ability of his family to care for. Shortly after the family decided that he would not return home, Mrs D died. Since then only one son visits and then only occasionally. He has five other children who were all involved in his care while his wife was alive.

Workers need to be alert to the possibility of the person with dementia becoming the scapegoat in families with problems. Matrimonial problems can often be avoided and all the tensions blamed on the person with dementia. It can also work the other way round when, for example, an adolescent child takes the blame for a family under stress because of a relative with dementia.

Finally we need to address the need for intervention skills. Many people with dementia and their carers refuse help: often at a time where a little bit of help would prevent breakdown later.

It is very easy to irretrievably damage the fragile care networks that sustain elderly people with dementia. At the early stages when the person with dementia is coping but worrying about the future it is easy to undermine them by offering too much help. This is the point, however, at which good relationships can be established in a preventive sense. Links with agencies which can pick up situations before they reach crisis point can replace hours of struggling with impossible situations later. In the middle stages it is essential to build up the knowledge, skills and confidence of the carers so that the person with dementia is helped, to do as much as possible. In the advanced stages, radical changes need to be made with a minimum of upheaval lest unnecessary hurt is inflicted on both the sufferer and the carer. The physical and emotional health of many carers is irretrievably damaged by too little help too late.

Carers are not of course always people with the best motivation. Sometimes they live with a person with dementia because it is the only source of housing. Sometimes they are benefitting financially. Sometimes they may be physically or sexually abusing the person with dementia. Difficult judgements may have to be made weighing up the pros and cons of supporting existing care networks. *Mrs R* and *Mrs J* illustrate how difficult this can be.

Mrs R a sixty-five year old woman with mild dementia and double incontinence had a man friend who, until recently, had taken charge of her money. However, a social worker had discovered that he had been withdrawing large sums of money from her building society accounts in order, he said, to pay bills and finance her car so that he could take her out. The woman was aware that he was doing this but did not seem to wish to prevent it. The social worker was unable to find evidence of bills which he had paid with the money. Mrs R allowed the social workers to negotiate an arrangement with the building society in an effort to reduce the number of withdrawals but was adamant that she wanted to retain control of her money. Meanwhile, money continued to be withdrawn.

Mrs J is 86 years old. She lives with her son and daughter-in-law, the house belongs to Mrs J. Her son is 55 years old, his wife is 10 years younger. She has undergone treatment for depression and anxiety in the past.

Mr J rang the hospital social work department asking for help. He had had dealings with a hospital social worker when his mother had been in hospital six months previously. Mr J said that he was forced to hit his mother for the things she said, he had to 'slap her face to knock some sense into her'. This request for help was passed to the social services area team.

Mrs J is physically fit, being mobile and managing the steep stairs of the terraced house without difficulty. She has some short-term memory loss, for example, she had forgotten that her son was married, she thought that he lived with a woman outside marriage. Mrs J has problems recalling dates, but knows approximately how old she is and also where she lives. On occasion Mrs J has carried faeces into her bedroom, and when left alone has turned on gas taps, leaving them unlit.

The relationship between Mrs J and her daughter-in-law seems fraught. Mrs J has a sharp tongue and enjoys an argument. More often than not some of her remarks have provoked her son and daughter-in-law too far. Mrs J said, "I can't open my mouth without getting a clout."

Mr and Mrs J (junior) acknowledge that Mrs J does not always do or say things deliberately, but still appear to believe that shouting at her or hitting her will stop this behaviour.

It is tragically easy to cease being client centred when we are under pressure. It is too easy to make quick decisions and to take action which undermines or even destroys relationships between cared for and carer. Keeping a level head requires very complex skills in analysing the situation and targeting our effort, planning the way help will be offered and provided over what may be a long period, standing beside our clients against other people or agencies, remaining purposeful in the midst of conflict and providing a quality of intervention that from the outset builds trust between ourselves and our clients. These are skills of the highest level and we need to be sure that this is recognised by those who manage our services.

Management has a key role in setting the client centred department structure and approach. One aspect of this is user involvement which can be broken down into:

1) The issue of users of services both people with dementia and their carers: their participation and control.

2) The issue of access to services.

3) The range of choice of services that can be made available.

4) The quantity and quality of information about services that is easily available.

These issues raise questions about the way we organise professional help. There are undoubtedly the winds of change blowing but they tend to be small scale initiatives rather than a major rethink of basic structures and approaches. We need, for example, mechanisms for listening to carers around which services can be fitted. The key words are flexibility, better communication, partnership and training to change attitudes.

At present most of our work structures are going through a period of incremental change and are facing fundamental change. Whether this makes them more 'user friendly' remains to be seen although that is a stated aim.

Resource Management
In the ideal world, workers would be supported by agencies which provided ample and suitable residential care homes. domiciliary

services would be flexibly provided to include week-end cover. There would be a night-sitting service which would enable carers to get a good night's rest. Host families would provide one form of short term care. Care assistants could move into a house to care for it and the person with dementia to avoid the confusion of transfer to short term care. There would be lunch clubs and day centres with efficient transport and a positive, rehabilitative outlook. There is a need for resource centres, maybe with bedrooms, that could provide day care, assessment and co-ordinate community outreach. The full range of skilled professional help would be available wherever the person with dementia lived. There would be flexible funding to meet needs not otherwise catered for, and workers would do more preventive and planned work and less crisis work. There would be time to remove the myths and misapprehensions that relatives and the person with dementia may have about residential care. The health services would have more day hospital places, and more accessible geriatric and psychogeriatric assessment beds with plenty of skilled staff. The GP would be communicating with a good psychogeriatrician with beds for rotating care, and good liaison would give both access to carer support groups and to good community nursing. The whole range of services would be backed up by a specialist community dementia mental health team.

But we do not live in an ideal world and resource management is often a problem of making the best of poor resources. However, there is a responsibility, in managing resources, to ensure that they are designed to meet the assessed needs of clients. The tasks of resource management, resource rationing and needs assessment must be kept separate. If they are vested in the same person, they must not be allowed to dictate practice in the wrong direction. The right direction is to assess needs, develop resources on the basis of those needs and to ration in accordance with those needs. Managers of resources have a duty to act as advocate for greater resources if assessed as needed by practitioners. Needs must dictate resources, NOT vice-versa.

It is important for all units and departments to have a *written* policy for meeting the needs of people with dementia in respect of field and residential services, and support from voluntary and private agencies. In compiling these policies gaps and overlaps will be identified and a pooling of resources will be much more realistic. This is, of course, best done in close collaboration with other agencies. There should also be easily accessible and updated information about local resources available to both workers and clients.

The King's Fund, in their book *Living Well in Old Age* (1986) have most usefully worked out for managers of services the implications of their principles listed earlier. They have done this in the form of twenty key questions. Managers need to be able to answer all these questions in a written policy, so they are presented in full below.

Implications for Managers and Planners

Twenty Key Questions
Principle 1
People with dementia have the same human value as anyone else irrespective of their degree of disability or dependence.

Recognising the status and worth of people with dementia.

1) Have the health and local authorities established a senior leadership group with clear responsibility for overseeing the development of the total local service for people with dementia?

2) Have all members of this leadership group been involved in agreeing the principles and values which will underlie the services? How has this set of principles been disseminated among authority members, professional staff and community organisations? How are they used in activities such as staff recruitment or training?

3) Have the authorities set up effective arrangements for quality assurance in the day-to-day running of services? How are services being monitored against the agreed principles and values?

Principle 2
People with dementia have the same varied human needs as anyone else.

Responding to a full range of needs within the mainstream of society.

4) Are people with dementia denied access (for whatever reason) to generic health and local authority services? How is this situation reviewed?

5) How do senior managers review the system of services for people with dementia as a whole? How are resources allocated across different areas of activity – assessment and case planning, treatment, long-term support, crisis services, and so on – and how is the overall balance of priorities decided?

6) Have the authorities set up a number of small planning teams which are sufficiently 'near the ground' to involve staff who know individual service users well, and to involve local people with knowledge of neighbourhood resources?

7) Have resources been allocated to set up and support local forums where a wide range of professionals and agencies can meet regularly to maintain contact and co-ordinate their activities?

8) Have financial, manpower and staff management systems been created to focus service planning in each of the smaller localities which make up the authority?

9) In allocating the budget, does the authority give a clear priority to employing staff who will work with people with dementia in a variety of ordinary settings – their own homes, GPs' surgeries, local recreational facilities, and so on – in preference to investing in special purpose-built facilities? How do the two sums compare at the moment and how are they reviewed?

Principle 3

People with dementia have the same rights as other citizens.
  Promoting the rights of people who use the services.

10) What attempts have been made to find out the user's views about the service offered?

11) What guidance or training has been provided for staff to identify individual preferences and offer meaningful choices to people with very severe disabilities?

12) What arrangements have been made to provide access to independent representation and advocacy (for example through the CHC, a law centre, CABS of citizen advocacy projects particularly for people with dementia who are highly dependent? What channels are used to monitor and investigate complaints?

Principle 4

Every person with dementia is an individual.
  Creating individual-centred services.

13) How do resources allocated to schemes serving people with dementia as individuals or in small groups (that is, less than six) compare with allocations to larger projects (that is, buildings and campuses for 20, 50 or more)?

14) How are the deficiences and problems picked up by staff planning individual care programmes collated and made available to the leadership group?

15) How much extra training and professional and personal support have been provided for staff who are required to undertake a more flexible and individualised style of working?

16) Have all members of the senior leadership group spent at least eight hours of a day in the company of a person with a severe degree of dementia?

Principle 5

People with dementia have the right to forms of support which don't exploit family and friends.
  Safeguarding the rights and quality of life of families and other carers.

17) What procedures are followed to make sure that carers are fully involved in assessments and in drawing up individual care plans for people with dementia.

18) Have independent studies of the views and experiences of carers been carried out within the authority and how has the information been used?

19) Has a comprehensive information and advice service been set up which can be used by carers? Has a system of support and representation been established for carers which is independent of the professional services and separate from advocacy arrangements for people with dementia?

20) Have places been made available for carers to participate in service planning activities at local and central level?

Engaging the Interest and Commitment of the Client and All Concerned

People with dementia need security but not at the expense of reasonable stimulation. They should be helped to celebrate small victories and moments of clarity in order to enhance their self esteem. Without memory and the capacity to interpret everyday happenings the world becomes a frightening and threatening place. As the disease progresses the feeling of self worth is further limited. Therefore the aim should be to develop their remaining skills and to help them to remain involved in their surroundings and to prevent the world slipping away.

This can be achieved by involving them in activities that are within their capabilities if they enjoy them. Music and music-making, sing-alongs, music and movement, exercises, active games, walking (with a companion – not just wandering). All can be helpful and enjoyable. Simple cookery and preparation, helping the staff or carer with household chores. Things like sorting packs of cards or shelling peas. Anything that makes them feel wanted is helpful. Gardening, which could include indoor gardens and window boxes is a valued activity. These are just a few ideas.

James Thomas, the man quoted in Cohen and Eisdorfer's book *The Loss of Self* (1988) who kept a diary of his feelings as Alzheimer's Disease developed writes, 'I am hungry for the life that is being taken away from me. I am a human being, I still exist. I have a family. I hunger for friendship, happiness and the touch of a loved hand. What I ask for is that what is left of my life shall have some meaning. Give me something to die for. Help me to be strong and free until my self no longer exists.'

There is often a tendency in any professional to blame clients if they fail to trust us. Cases can even be closed because the client refuses help. This is more than usually likely in work with people with dementia who can fail to understand what is being offered and can also be very fearful of any change at all given a fragile grip on reality. Carers too are often unwilling to relinquish care to someone they do not fully trust or to services they see as being less than satisfactory. Alternatively relatives are so relieved to get any help that they insist it is all 'wonderful' and will not insist on the quality and type of care they really need. A close involvement of carers in planning the nature and provision of services can make the services more responsive to clients' needs. The worker is usually however the person with access to many sources of help and has to use a trusting relationship to make the link between client and service. Trust arises from many sources: respect, communication skills, genuine empathy and warmth as well as being trustworthy. It is very important to be clear and honest in offering help to people who are often bewildered and extremely anxious. A good working relationship is a lot easier if the referral has been received early enough. It is invaluable to have established a relationship before major changes in life style are considered.

Mr T's dementia had been progressing over several years and in the last few years had been treating his wife very violently imagining himself back in the prisoner of war camp he had been in as a young man. Mrs T told nobody about his behaviour until after a particularly severe beating she walked out of the house with her suitcase packed. Two days later Mr T was found and admitted to hospital. Mrs T was found but was too distraught to take her husband home. He contracted pneumonia after a few weeks and died leaving Mrs T feeling very guilty indeed.

Therapeutic pessimism can easily result from referrals that take place in a crisis. Mrs T illustrates the need to have a good referral system. GPs can provide this if they trust the worker and understand dementia. If teamwork does not exist, regular, systematic feedback can build trust between professionals.

Another factor in engaging commitment is the lack of status that applies to work with old people. This causes workers not to want to take on dementia problems and to treat them as second class referrals. So the status of work, and lack of resources and time for preventive work results in pessimism about the outcome.

Agency structures which encourage workers to take up the rights issues, to undertake real preventive work and to receive recognition for their involvement with old people can encourage optimism. Optimism is essential to positive practice.

Moving into Care
In the earlier sections of this book a great deal of stress was put on the transition into permanent, long term 24-hour care. In this brief section some practical advice is given. 24-hour care may not mean care in an

institution, although it usually does. Many areas now have family placement schemes where elderly people can stay in the Scheme carer's home for a short period of time or even on a permanent basis to give the relatives a break. This type of homely, individual care is often more suitable for people with dementia, than going into an institution for a short period. Although carers for these schemes have always been carefully vetted, the key to success seems to be accurate matching of ·carer and cared for and the availability of 24 hour support for the carers.

There are some schemes available that provide boarding-in care, which allows the elderly person to stay in their own home and provides a substitute Scheme carer to take over, while their relative is away. This is probably the most appropriate respite care for people with dementia because it is the least disruptive and disturbing.

Transitions are very stressful for people with dementia who cannot always 'make sense' of what is going on. The greatest care has to be taken from the beginning. First the difficult business of matching the person to the establishment. Workers should know as much as possible about available establishments in terms of their knowledge and facilities for care of people with dementia, the quality of the amenities and staff and in terms of the ambience and the other residents. Some element of choice may be possible for the person with dementia although this will undoubtedly be hard to organise and may require trial stays. The process of admission needs very careful handling. There should have been a number of visits and an overnight stay when this seems helpful although for some people this can be too upsetting. Flexibility and sensitivity are the keys to a successful transition.

The transition can be just as stressful for the professional worker who may have known the family for a number of years and worked hard at maintaining the client/patient at home. Long stay hospital wards are seldom ideal and may produce feelings of angst for the worker. This may affect the process because boundaries remain unclear between the role of the community based worker and the hospital workers. This may be confusing to the family and the person with dementia.

Whatever the long term setting an admission meeting to include the professionals, where roles are made explicit followed by an informal review to include family and person with dementia one or two weeks after admission may relieve the inevitable stresses.

It is especially important to people with dementia that they can take furniture and belongings; perhaps even pets. The new place must feel like a real home with enough about it that is familiar to help them settle down.

The transitional phase itself is confusing for anybody – but obviously more so for someone with dementia. Expectations must be low but positive with plenty of patience and time to settle. The role of carers during this period is crucial. They need to feel responsible. Professionals can take over and leave carers feeling impotent. The early identification of a key worker from among the residential staff can ease the transitional phase for the person with dementia and the carer. It also aids the key worker in building a profile of the new resident and their family. With this it becomes possible to see the person with dementia as someone with a past, a present and a future.

Mrs E entered a specialist residential home from a psychiatric setting with major problems of anxiety. These were modified through building up of close strong relationships with the key worker. She developed trust and confidence and was thereby less dependent on staff and was making clear decisions in respect of her life. Via this strong bond she went through a process of day care and was discharged into a conventional care setting more suited to her needs. The support links existed for some time after that. After nine months of this lifestyle Mrs E required hospitalisation due to physical problems. This condition created marked mental change and the conventional home requested re-admission to the specialist home for Mrs E. The input of the key worker again assisted her to regain the lost 'skills': building up her confidence, increasing her social interaction and giving her as full a life as possible under the circumstances.

Groupwork
Groups with people with dementia are generally part of reality orientation, reminiscence or recall and are fully covered in the next section. Here then a brief word about groups for carers.

Groups for carers can have many purposes. Age Concern Scotland has produced a step by step guide to setting up groups for carers in the book *Reaching Out to Dementia Sufferers and Their Carers* (1986). Groups of carers may appreciate information. They may provide opportunities to share the pain and unhappiness, to share skills and experience, to have a good laugh – a luxury that is only really possible with other people who understand. The essential value of these groups is the realisation for the carer that they are not alone. The groups are often, but by no means always, set up by professionals. Many begin as, or turn into Alzheimers Disease Society/Alzheimer's Scotland groups. Workers may choose to run the more exclusive kind of groups, for example those for wives or single daughters if they feel there are special needs to be considered. All purpose carers' groups can also be of great value and diminish 'competition'.

Mrs A looked after her confused aunt, for whom she was the only next of kin, as long as she could but she had to relinquish care because she was also looking after a husband and children. She felt very guilty about this and was pleased to be invited to attend a five session group for relatives of patients at the longstay psychiatric hospital where her aunt was a patient. She was astonished and delighted to discover from the other relatives that her aunt's behaviour was similar to many others, and that they too felt guilty. She had never been told that her aunt had dementia and that her behaviour was part of the disease. The relatives invited a psychiatrist to attend their group and obtained great comfort and insight when he described the progress of the disease.

The social aspect of any carers' group should never be neglected. Many carers and their relatives become isolated sometimes because friends shun them. They can also have problems going out if, for example, a husband or wife is unable to cope alone in a public convenience or on public transport. One function of a carers' group can be to organise social events. Any group should be local and accessible. When this is the case practical help is often given to fellow members in the form of transport or support when the person with dementia is admitted to long term care.

Pressure must never be put on relatives to attend a group. Some people are not comfortable in groups, others are frightened of hearing what is in store for them. The offer must remain open so that if a carer begins to feel the need to share experiences with other carers, the opportunity is there. Many members find it difficult to leave the group after the death of the person with dementia because of the comradeship and support they have experienced.

The nature of the group will vary vastly depending on its size, style and members. Many groups have a formal speaker. The sharing and mutual support happens afterwards with the tea and biscuits. Plenty of time must be allowed at the end if this is the plan for the group.

Reminiscence and Recall and Reality Orientation
Since the early 1980s there has been throughout the United Kingdom a growing interest in using reminiscence 'the act or process of recalling the past' to enrich the lives of older people, including those with dementia. The publication of recall packages opened the way for many people from various professional backgrounds to begin to understand the rich possibilities inherent in the common everday processes of reminiscence.

Reminiscence is not only used by old people but it seems to serve important purposes in late life. Because we all come to accommodate to our pasts in ways which serve to make the present tolerable, people should never be pushed into either group or individual reminiscence against their wishes for reminiscence does not suit everyone. People are their own best judge of whether or not they wish to reminisce about their past.

Reminiscence serves many different purposes and the uses which people make of reminiscence processes will be very varied. It encourages self-worth, that all important sense that you count for something. As old people buy into the myths and stereotypes about ageing which abound they are all too willing to write themselves off. By reminding them of their long past they may be helped to retain a sense of their own significance as a unique individual.

Linked to self-worth is a sense of self-identity which may be confirmed by reminiscence. A strong sense of person identity appears to be important as people age because as they value themselves, so others will value them. A sense of personal significance helps people retain a sense of control over their own lives. In dementing illness this sense of personal identity and along with it a sense of self-worth is eroded. By reminding people of who they have been in the past it may help them to hang onto a sense of who they are in the present.

Reminiscence assists the process of life review. As people age they tend to look back, review the past and 'put their house in order', reworking old unresolved conflicts and facing up to the major developmental task of late life, namely preparation for death. Reviewing and reworking the past can therefore be regarded as a sign of mental health, rather than mental ill health. Reminiscence indicates that an older person is behaving in ways appropriate to the stage of life they have reached and is working on age related developmental tasks.

Reminiscence encourages and enriches social exchange. People are helped to discover common experiences, shared interests and are motivated to embark on new or enriched relationships through the experience of shared reminiscence. Especially for those who care for people with dementia, reminiscence is a way of finding out about the uniqueness of each person and it becomes a way of sharing in the life of that person. Instead of being preoccupied with the frailty and deficits of the person with dementia as experienced in the present, reminiscence shows you how they used to be. It enlarges our sympathies, encourages our respect, increases our understanding and transforms our relationships.

Without some knowledge of a person's past it is impossible to assess the level of their present functioning. Knowledge about a person's past illuminates our understanding of them in the present and helps carers devise individual care plans which are more likely to be effective because they are based on detailed knowledge of past interests, abilities and experience. People with dementia require detailed individualised care plans which help them to make the most of the healthy or relatively healthy aspects of their cognitive and social abilities. Reminiscence is the key to making such plans because it means that long-term memory can be used as a guide to what is more likely, rather than less likely to capture the person's attention in the present.

Finally reminiscence is mostly an enjoyable experience. It is easily encouraged and can be used in both planned and spontaneous ways with either individuals or groups in many different settings. It does not require any particular equipment although the skilful use of triggers can both accelerate and enrich the recall process. It is not the monopoly of any one profession and may be used with mutual benefit by formal and informal carers in people's own homes, substitute homes, clubs, social centres, day centres, and residential homes, nursing homes and hospitals of many kinds.

Reminiscence is frequently equated with *Reality Orientation*. Although in practice both these approaches may resemble each other and each may shade into the other, they arise from different theoretical perspectives. Reminiscence or life review owes its origins to psychoanalysis, ego psychology, existentialism and phenomenology while reality orientation is firmly rooted in learning theory. The underlying values of both approaches are different. Reminiscence work conveys an unequivocal message that an interest in the past experience of people is valuable in its own right, that it is important in itself and for its own sake and that sharing that history is likely to benefit its teller and its hearers in various ways. Reality orientation stresses the present and values the past only insofar as it serves as a bridge to the present. Reminiscence demonstrates a willingness and capacity to enter into the past of the person with dementia. Reality orientation assists people with dementia join our present reality. People move continually between the present and the past and vice versa but because of the conceptual and value differences it is important for practitioners to be aware of these theoretical distinctions in order to reflect critically on their practice and improve their professional performance.

Reality orientation has encouraged the development of group work with people with dementia. Various group activities are used to stimulate people's interest in their present surroundings such as notices, games, calendars, clocks, consistent colour reinforcers and discussion of newspaper headlines and photographs. The emphasis, whether in small groups or in 24 hour total programmes tends to be didactic and is designed to consistently remind the old person of their own identity and their present reality in terms of people, place and time.

An excellent book on this subject has been written by Lorna Rimmer entitled *Reality Orientation Principles and Practice* published by Winslow Press (1982). Included in the book is an assessment which assists when commencing a group for reality orientation because according to the score achieved the group leader has guidance as to what level to aim the group. Patients find it very distressing being part of a group in which they are unable to participate. The book also contains many practical suggestions and ideas for anyone wishing to commence a reality orientation group.

24-hour reality orientation is most effective when used informally by all staff who come into contact with residents. Cooks, domestics and other workers carrying out routine duties can reinforce reality by talking about their work. Staff will need some preparation for this, and a consistent approach will need to be based on assessment and care planning. Holden *et al.*' useful short handbook *24-Hour Approach to the Problem of Confusion in Elderly People* (1983) published by the Winslow Press is an invaluable source of advice and encouragement and can form the basis of staff discussions and resident reviews.

Many residential and nursing staff are inclined to dismiss reminiscence as ineffectual because it fails to improve a person's memory for recent events and their present orientation in time and place. They dismiss too readily the intangible gains in sociability and sheer pleasure, even if soon forgotten which participation in reminiscence brings. To be able to reach into the private world of the person with severe dementia to offer them pleasure and enjoyment, a distraction from their wandering or a momentary shared exchange with another person are gains which should not be lightly dismissed. As research into dementia continues it is worth noting that neurobiological studies of ageing rats have identified organic changes in brain cells and their inter-connections, in rates provided with stimulating, compared to unstimulating environments. There is nothing to lose by investing time and energy in an approach to older people which is widely, if not universally acceptable to them. As we become more skilled in its applications, reminiscence offers a chance to impinge on the isolating, lonely, bleak, unstimulating, socially barren worlds inhabited by so many people with dementia.

Many people with dementia can participate in small reminiscence and reality orientation groups. People who are emotionally labile, hyperactive or easily moved to either verbal or physical aggression may need to be excluded from the group in favour of one to one work. However it is possible that in a group setting they may become more sociable and a chance could have been missed by exlcuding them from the start. A careful judgement is needed.

Because it is memory for recent events, places, people and time which is impaired, many people with dementia may appear exceedingly incompetent in their present functioning. Carers, burdened by the repeated demonstration of contemporary deficits, experience people with dementia as inadequate, incompetent, unrewarding and usually exceedingly demanding. As memory of the past, especially the distant past may be relatively intact and unaffected by the dementing processes, it is possible to key into this memory bank and help both the person with dementia and their carers derive pleasure and satisfaction from the processes of recall.

Even people with quite serious dementias can enjoy recall. Whole areas of their memory for the past may be relatively untouched by the dementia and people who are quite disoriented in present time and place may be exceedingly lucid about the past.

It is often possible for one or two people with dementia to participate in a so called normal reminiscence group. Such a group needs to be kept small, probably with no more than eight to ten members.

Communication will usually be enhanced in these circumstances if there is a co-worker to share the work. Lucid participation by members usually labelled as confused brings mutual pleasure in shared achievements and serves to alter others' negative views.

If for whatever reason it is not possible to include a person in a small group it may be possible to work with them individually. The careful selection of multi-sensory triggers closely related to their personal, social, and work backgrounds and interests may stimulate them to active recall and interestingly, often surprisingly coherent, reminiscence. Reality orientation too uses trigger material from the past and much of the material here which is used in reminiscence is also used in reality orientation to engage and stimulate people with dementia.

Some people may be so impaired that they are unable to name objects, let alone describe their use yet by their non-verbal behaviour they can demonstrate that they appreciate the nature and use of such objects. For example, if passed an iron they will draw their hand away or if they hear a familiar tune will emerge from lethargy and almost total isolation to tap their foot or hum. Many people who undertake reminiscence work with grossly impaired people report small, often dramatic, if short-lived examples of reaching inside somebody's private world to catch a glimpse of their earlier self. Such encounters encourage perseverance and are antidotes to therapeutic pessimism and despair.

A group consisting of people who all have memory difficulties should not be larger than three to five. The frequency of sessions, the time of day and the location in which the group meets are particularly important. Twice weekly or even daily sessions, rather than weekly sessions are suggested. The best time is often late in the morning or in the early afternoon when people with dementia are at their most receptive.

Rooms used for groupwork need to be small, comfortable, relatively private and free from distractions. Any member who grows restless and wishes to leave should be allowed to do so. Some may wander off and return at a later time but preventing their going may make them liable to become increasingly agitated.

Special places furnished and equipped according to an earlier period and rich in special associations have been created in some residential homes and hospitals. A homely kitchen, a pub or an ordinary living room evoke recall and promote associated social behaviour.

Communication with people with dementia is possible providing we are not intent on correcting historical detail, keeping people right and running a history class. It is more important to attend to the feelings underlying the communication and to the intent of the communication rather than to its exact content. Pleasure in participation, a sociable experience and shared understanding of a person's past life are all more important in this kind of work than historical accuracy.

The length of sessions must be adjusted according to the interest level of the group which will probably fluctuate from session to session. People may sustain their interest for an hour or more depending on the relevance of the triggers used. Many impaired people are able to converse with each other or to build on the contributions of others through associated recall. Sometimes, depending on the nature of impairment it may be difficult to discern evidence of the dementing process which reasserts itself once a demand for addressing present reality is re-imposed.

It is not suggested that we collude with a person's confusion but that we show a willingness to join their time perspective. If the older person talks as if the past is present, then we can join them where they are, always remembering to use the past tense when referring to time past.

Motivation is heightened if triggers are used which relate closely to the person's background, place of origin and interests. Questions need to be simple, never threatening or invasive and time needs to be given to listen to the answers. If a particular line of questioning is distressing it may be better abandoned but personal knowledge of the people you are working with is the best guide to sensitive, responsive, empathic practice. The important principle is that people should be helped to talk rather than placed in situations which expose their limitations.

The triggers need to appeal to all the senses of sight, sound, touch and smell in order to achieve the greatest possible stimulation. They need to evoke ordinary, everyday domestic, social, family and work experience. The more closely the triggers relate to the person's past experience, the richer is likely to be their response. The more local triggers are the more evocative they will be. They may relate to a theme, an event, an interest, occupation, people or places. There is almost no limit to what can be used. They may be used simultaneously but are probably best used sequentially. What appeals to one person may not necessarily prove effective with another. Therefore different approaches need to be tried with different individuals and groups. responses are vastly different depending on past experience, stored memories, the emotions vested in the memories recalled and the areas of the brain which may have been damaged by dementia. For these reasons multisensory triggers are likely to be more effective than triggers which rely on a single or a limited number of senses. It is a mistake to use too many triggers or to use them too quickly. Give people time and pace the presentation according to each situation.

Gibson suggests in *Reminiscence: A Training Pack* (1989) that adopting a thematic rather than chronological approach in understanding reminiscence with either individuals or groups is often more promising. Such themes might include the following:

School Days: Recorded sounds of a school bell, children reciting tables, or singing in morning assembly. Smells associated with the school nurse's visit such as methylated spirits. Memorabilia and artefacts like copy books, reading books, chalk, slates, ink wells or bottles and ink pens. Pictures and slides of school buildings, class groups and sports days.

Wartime: Recording of Vera Lynn singing the White Cliffs of Dover, other wartime songs and musicians like Gracie Fields or Glen Miller. Recordings of wartime speeches. Memorabilia and artefacts like ration books, identity cards, call up papers, uniforms, medals, gas masks, letters and diaries. Pictures or slides of wartime events, leaders, evacuation, sleeping in the underground, munitions factory workers and landgirls and troops returning home.

Family Life: Domestic themes like washday, shopping, holidays and recreation are powerfully evocative and a great deal of related trigger material is readily available. Babies, toddlers and small animals provide a marvellous stimulus to conversation and reminiscence. Many elderly people have been 'in service'.

Although many museums and public libraries are becoming increasingly interested in making their collections available to housebound and institutionalised old people it is very helpful to have your own modest collection of triggers ready to hand. Do not use grand antiques which people will be afraid of damaging. Use ordinary things which people may handle, pass to each other and examine at close quarters.

The sense of taste and smell diminishes with age and may be seriously impaired in people with Alzheimer Disease yet nevertheless smell is a useful means of encouraging recall. Smells can be put into small bottles and when passed around provide a great course of lively debate and argument. Similar and contrasting smells as well as different concentrations may all be used. Questions can then focus both on identification of the smell as well as on associated recollections.

Tastes and associated smells are useful triggers. For example particular sweets like brandy balls or conversation lozenges may be associated with childhood. Particular food may be associated with special events. Different ethnic backgrounds and dietary habits should all be catered for.

Visual material is readily available in books, magazines, newspapers, published slide packages like *Recall* and *Do You Mind the Time? Northern Ireland Recall Memory Joggers* and many other similar publications. Help the Aged, Age Exchange Reminiscence Project and the Winslow Press are all excellent sources of such materials.

Projected slides have an intrinsic appeal. Enlarged photographs enable close scrutiny and detailed examination. Video film if used for active, not passive viewing can be useful.

Music is especially helpful in working with people with dementia. Much recorded music of all periods is readily available on record and cassette and many public libraries will lend sound recordings. Singing along to either a tape or even better an instrument will stimulate spontaneous shared pleasure. Any latent talents in the group members should be utilised and opportunities provided for everyone to contribute. Music used for reminiscence may open up other possibilities. Opportunities to use instruments, even without prior experience can produce surprising results as the talents required for composition and performance may not be affected by short term memory impairment.

It is worth remembering that some people with severe expressive aphasia following strokes may still be able to sing even if they are unable to talk. People with dementia who have cased to speak can often sing perfectly well. Marshall (1983) points out that workers have got to be uninhibited and sing along.

Refreshments of various kinds served as part of the reminiscence activity help to make the occasion special and a change from ordinary routines. Food with rich associations of earlier times can be used effectively if time and circumstances permit.

Visits to places of past significance may stimulate recall and also give immense pleasure in the here and now. Hospital patients who on a ward behave in antisocial or unconventional ways when taken out visiting often behave quite appropriately. It is as if the environmental cues reactivate the forgotten appropriate behaviour. So often the institutionalised patient with dementia no longer is provided with the clues and cues to call forth the appropriate social behaviour. They are not being difficult when they behave antisocially on the ward. Rather they have lost the capacity or mental agility to remember what is appropriate in very routine ridden situations which make few social demands on them. A minibus can be used very creatively if it is driven to familiar places.

Much more could be written about both the possibilities and problems of undertaking reminiscence work with people with dementia. It is important not to make exaggerated claims but it is equally important to encourage carers of all kinds to explore its rich possibilities. Formal and informal carers, professionals as well as family members and volunteers need to be encouraged to venture out, to have a go, to risk attempting something rather than nothing. Any response no matter how small or how seemingly transitory should not be dismissed. Anything which improves the social interaction between people with dementia and those who live and work with them holds out hope. It challenges boredom, gives pleasure and provides the possibility for counteracting the prevailing sense of mutual grief caused by loss of past competence. Anything which improves the respect, warmth and affection extended to people with dementia promises to push back the boundaries of their isolating disease and helps them to escape, if only momentarily from the prison of their private world.

Problem Identification
This is put in as a special section because one of the questions to keep asking is: Whose problem is this?

This question must be asked repeatedly. Whose problem is it when a person with dementia takes all their clothes off in the street? Whose problem is it when a person with dementia's table manners offend other residents in an old people's home? There is always a tendency to blame the client. Feelings of fury, frustration and helplessness have to be directed somewhere and the easiest victim is the client. 'Systems Thinking' and be helpful especially if the identification of systems and the plan for action is done by those most involved. However, simply asking the question is an important first step.

Whose problem, for example, is the chaos that ensues when a dementia case hits a social services local office? This panic is unnecessary if the workers are experienced and trained in this area of work. The chaos is partially due to referrals taking place at a time of crisis and also to the tendency for departments to give this area of work a low priority. There is a need for good team management that will ensure support for workers given difficult cases. There is a need for specialist training, not just with dealing with dementia but with crisis intervention. There is a need for developmental work with other professionals and communities to encourage referral prior to a crisis. There is a need for adequate staffing and policy to respond to such referrals. With these requirements met there would be little chaos. It is therefore a management responsibility to deal with the lack of policy and planning and a worker responsibility to deal with the referral.

In the more general sense actually working out specific responsibilities for dealing with specific problems both within the particular setting and between professionals working together can lead to a sharing of responsibility and an agreement to split up tasks into areas which people feel are manageable. It is often the sheer overwhelming enormity of the task that causes people to feel hopeless, helpless and to withdraw. Each agency needs to create support and supervision mechanisms which will support staff.

Clients' Rights

The rights of a person with dementia deserve the same respect as a person suffering from any other mental disorder. These are enshrined in the Mental Health Act 1983, Mental Health (Scotland) Act 1984 and the Mental Health (Northern Ireland) Order 1986. There seems to be a widespread unwillingness to use the law with people with dementia even when they are a danger to themselves and others. Whilst each situation has to be considered separately, it may be the case that their rights would be better protected by the use of the law in some circumstances.

There is a common tendency for society to believe that elderly people need protecting and that their rights to choose are secondary to this. Workers need to be aware of this attitude and to act on behalf of the right of people to determine their own life.

69

However a dilemma arises with dementia in that it is possible that a point will be reached when a person can no longer function sufficiently well to make these decisions. Workers should aim to help their client to reach the decision they would have made if able to. In effect the worker may occasionally have to make the decision on this basis. This is a difficult path to tread, only made easier by previous knowledge of the client. There may be historical evidence of the wishes of an individual by which the worker should be guided.

It is usually unacceptable to take advantage of advancing dementia to impose a lifestyle that would not have been accepted by that person.

It is necessary, if institutional care is thought to be needed in the future, to discuss this with the person and ascertain if they would be willing to accept it, should they deteriorate beyond being able to decide. Given the difficulties with this many older people like to specify while they are still hale and hearty. Should they say they would not accept it then their wishes have to be respected. Many accept it and then regret the decision which they made without full information which is why Age Concern has produced Bland's book *Residential Care: Is It For Me?* (1987).

Death and Bereavement

Old age and its resulting disabilities must not be viewed as inevitable and untreatable. Much of the neglect that arises from inadequate practice by professionals is caused by an unwritten and unspoken dependence upon death to resolve the problems. Such attitudes increase the handicapping of many old people and could be avoided. Old age is not a problem to be resolved by death but a period of life to be enhanced by care for the frailties that sometimes accompany it. Death is a process that should not be ignored. Workers should be helping their clients (usually carers at this stage) by easing their feelings and fears. This does not imply sweetening a bitter pill but giving assistance, practical and emotional, to meet the needs that may arise at this stage of life.

There is an emerging debate about the 'living will' which is when a person in good mental health specifies in writing what they wish to happen if they are very ill and unable to make a rational decision. Many people feel they would like to specify that they do not want active treatment with antibiotics or force feeding if they are very ill, very frail and have dementia. The living will is a highly controversial issue because the opportunities for abuse are so obvious. However even without it, carers and professionals can face difficult decisions about when to provide very active, lifesaving intervention. Frank and open discussion is required between all those involved in these circumstances.

Death can be the point where relatives realise, what they have never really believed, that their relative with dementia ceased to known who they were. Often they believe that in the last moments, they were recognised again. It is probably a great comfort to believe this given the prolonged loss experience this kind of caring can be.

Relatives have to experience losing someone they care for long before the body dies because the personality and intellectual changes can be so fundamental. This is very stressful. It is an unresolved state of living bereavment. Sometimes they can feel, at death, as if they have already done their grieving. Counselling following the death, can be very helpful given these complexities and the fact that the emotional and physical strain of caring, often leaves the carer very run-down and exhausted. Sometimes, for example, it can take years to get sleep patterns re-established. The carer who has supported someone with dementia up to his/her death may need particularly sensitive help in the mourning period. After a prolonger period of strain accompanied by grieving for the loss while in life of the personality of the loved person, a frozen kind of numbness may continue after death. Recovering his/her own identity may prove difficult for the carer and many continue to find support in Alzheimer's Disease Society/Alzheimer's Scotland meetings. Isolation is the main problem after the death and the workers often have to help the carer pick up the pieces of life again. Carers can also feel guilty or be imposed upon by non-carers who feel guilty. They may need guidance in dealing with this.

Many relatives retain a fear of dementia for themselves. The extent to which it is an inherited illness is not known, though it is thought to be only slight. They may need an opportunity to talk through these worries.

Chapter 9

Individual Treatment and Management

This section looks at how carers both at home and in day or 24 hour care settings can best provide an environment that meets their needs as well as the needs of those for whom they are responsible. Clearly all the other sections of this book apply but this section sweeps with a broader brush. Although only about 5% of the elderly population are in formal 24-hour care of one sort or another a high proportion of those in care will have dementia. Large numbers of frail older people attend day units of some kind or another but precise figures are not available because of problems of definition. Treatment for people with dementia may not always amount to very much since we are talking about a progressive disease. However good management of relationships, the environment and time can make an enormous difference to how dementia is experienced by all concerned. Behaviour that is highly distressing such as incontinence, a catastrophic reaction, wandering and aggression can often be lessened. Before going on further about settings it is useful to look more closely at how this works in practice.

Incontinence

Being unable to control the bladder and eventually the bowels breaks one of society's fundamental taboos around personal cleanliness. Incontinence is humiliating for the sufferer, embarrassing for the relatives, and anxiety provoking for both. Many people with dementia resort to denial early on, ignoring the 'accident', routinely drying damp and wet clothing to wear it again, thus augmenting the problem of odour. This denial may extend to an incapacity to cope with pads and portable urinals effectively. Faeces may be hidden in drawers, disposed of down sinks or in waste bins. Soiled clothing may be hidden or thrown away.

The analysis of the symptoms of incontinence, stress incontinence, urgency and frequency, overflow incontinence with severe constipation a contributory cause, and reflex incontinence, shows that the first step in control is to differentiate between the symptoms. It could be that a sufferer might experience all these different forms in the coursed of the disease.

It is suggested that some problems with incontinence may occur relatively early in the onset of the disease, while the person is still quite active and able to enjoy walks and family outings. The short term memory failure, together with the mechanism of denial combine to make managing this early continence problematic for carers. However the loss of central incontinence comes later. In the early stages medical, social and psychological causes should be fully investigated before ascribing the condition to the process of the disease.

There is a powerful emotional element in caring for a family member who is quite unaware of bodily functions. Such a person may be taken to the lavatory, but needs to have someone there reminding him/her what to do, and may be unable to assess when the urination or evacuation is complete. Disgust and incest barriers may be breached, so intimate is the kind of care that may be needed. Workers need to be able to allow carers to express some of the feelings around these aspects of incontinence care, together with exploring the heavy burdens of washing, drying and replacing bedding, clothing and footwear. It needs enormous strength to continue, to maintain the dignity and integrity of the sufferer despite all this. Yet many carers probably feel it is the ultimate humiliation to reveal such matters to outsiders.

In dealing with incontinence the first rule is that there are a whole lot of causes and these must be identified. It could be arthritis and an inability to get out of the chair quickly enough. It is often linked to constipation. Sometimes a urinary tract infection is the cause. Quite often low morale is the key factor (perhaps linked to constipation). First find out *why* because the subsequent action depends on the cause. GPs and health visitors are the key professionals. For an arthritic the answer may be a riser chair, for the constipated a change of diet or medication. Medication too is needed for the urinary tract infection. Some people may not know where the lavatory is so better signing is required. Some people will read the sign without understanding and will require taking into the lavatory. Others may need a toiletting programme. Some may still require pads and aids. Lots of fluids during the day (but less in the evening) can be advised in most cases. Incontinence advisors from health authorities can be immensely helpful people.

Catastrophic Reaction
A catastrophic reaction is often exhibited by a person with dementia. Gwyther (1985) provides the following explanation and advice on preventing it. 'A situation that overwhelms the dementia patient can lead to a reaction that is out of proportion to the situation. New places, loud noises, new people and large groups, or uncertainty about a task, may lead to an excessive emotional reaction such as weeping, shouting, or striking out.

- Try to avoid stressful situations that may trigger catastrophic reactions.
- If a task is becoming too difficult, simplify it or redirect the person to another activity.
- Do not force participation in an activity if the person is resisting.
- Do not ask an upset individual to make decisions.
- Identify and, if possible, avoid situations that have led to catastrophic reactions in the past.
- When a catastrophic reaction occurs, stay calm. Do not overreact; your nervousness or anxiety can heighten the tension in an already tense situation.
- Try to avoid sudden moves to avoid frightening the person with dementia.
- Reduce confusion around him/her.
- Remove him/her from the distressing situation if possible.
- Cautiously distract his/her attention with an activity that he/she can easily do and enjoys.
- Even very angry people can respond to reassurance. A calm statement like, 'I know that you are upset and I want to help you' may defuse the situation. Hold and touch when appropriate.
- Restrain only if absolutely necessary.
- Forgetfulness can be a benefit in these situations because the memory impaired individual may quickly forget the episode.'

Wandering

Wandering causes much concern among staff. These concerns are legitimate. There are strategies which can help minimise them but in using these we must ensure that the basic rights of older people with dementia are not neglected.

Some facts to be stated first are as follows: wandering is rarely a regular or persistent feature in all people with dementia. (However, in units where two or three folk are wandering staff will think otherwise.) It often has a set time pattern.

There tend to be two kinds of wandering:

1) Directed – the walker is going to a specific place.
2) Beat-pounding – pacing up and down the same area to the point of exhaustion. This is a restless walk rather than a journey. It is not always 'aimless' as is often suggested.

Staff must examine their own attitudes to this very real issue and it must be recognised that very often it is seen as 'a nuisance', 'a frustration' or 'a tiresome task'. Often too we are fearful that we can 'lose face' with relatives, neighbours, other professionals and indeed colleagues if someone wanders off from our shift.

Our response to the person who wanders off, or who is attempting to wander, is very important in our successful management of that person's lifestyle. Our empathy with the person must extend to knowing how the person sees themselves i.e. the anxious mother hurrying to pick up the children, the housewife going home to make the family's tea, the person going out to collect the messages from the shops, going out to visit a family member, friend or to the church, a person who loves the open air being confined by the building, needing the toilet and being afraid to ask strangers or the person searching for their lost world, house, furniture or other treasures.

Staff therefore find themselves faced with a whole host of possible explanations as to why this person wishes or needs to leave the building. There are probably practical considerations to the person leaving the unit such as the likelihood of accidents and physical violence. The person is so fixed on leaving they will attempt to leave by whatever method presents itself such as climbing out of windows, pushing open fire doors, approaching visitors and asking them to help, phoning for the police and so on.

How then can we as staff intervene when faced with these tragic situations not just once but several times in the course of a shift.

1) A detailed knowledge of the person's history helps, knowing who is who in the person's life enables us to be fully aware to whom the person is referring. Knowledge of where they lived and when they lived there will assist in ascertaining where they are at in terms of recall ability. Such information needs to be built up with the resident, family and key worker working together. This knowledge enables staff to make a calm reassured response to the resident, and the fact that someone is familiar with their life does help to ease the resident's need to wander off. It also prevents staff having to 'think on their feet' for an acceptable reason why the person should not leave the building or should return to it with them. Such preparation and gathering of information is time-consuming. However, it is well worth the effort spent when it successfully enables us to assist the resident.

Following a six month hospital stay, 84 year old *Mr L* was admitted to a residential establishment. He was diagnosed as having a moderate to severe degree of dementia and had been a widower for approximately five years. During the first three months of residence he made several attempts to leave the home alone. At first staff were unsure of his intentions but then realised he was making for his house where he had lived for fifty years. His family were very unhappy about his wandering and blamed staff for not having a locked door and a more secure system for the residents. During a meeting with the family it was suggested Mr L return to his house for a goodbye visit. The family were reluctant to comply with this suggestion as it would be too emotionally upsetting for Mr L and he may even refuse to return to the home. However, after much gentle persuasion and reassurance the family agreed to take him home to choose belongings and say goodbye. Following two visits Mr L was able to speak about leaving his home and made no further attempts to wander away from the home.

2) Photographs of family and friends clearly marked with names are a useful and purposeful distraction from the focus to wander.

3) An ongoing diary completed with the resident/relatives and staff assisting is another tool which can prove helpful. If daughter Betty writes her address as 56 Parkhouse Road, Glasgow, it could help prevent the resident heading off for 62 Court Road, Ayr, where they stayed 25 years ago. Telephone numbers of relatives clearly written are often helpful. When the resident can phone her son or daughter this often lessens the urge/need to wander. Life story books with photographs are now being used with old people, as with children in care.

4) Time strategies are helpful and require a clear knowledge of when the possible need/urge to wander occurs. This must be identified and appropriate intervention organised to take place around that time. For example, if a person at 4.00 p.m. feels the need to go home and prepare the tea, involve them in a similar type of task in the unit such as filling milk jugs, sugar, jam, butter dishes. Similarly if at 10.00 a.m. they think they should be going out to collect the messages, take them to the shops and collect items needed by others. If at 8.00 p.m. they feel they need to go home and put children to bed, get them to assist in the bed chores, turning down beds, putting in hot water bottles, closing room curtains and so forth. These are all areas which have a link with the focus of the wandering and can divert from the need to leave.

5) Other diversional techniques are similar to the above but are extended to meet the needs in different situations. It is always of value for the staff group to discuss and review these in the light of individual experiences. Possibilities include a walk around the grounds with the residents, or longer and more vigorous walks if

the person is very active, collecting and arranging flowers for the person's room, visiting the local shops and actually making a purchase, working with the gardener, giving the man who is physically strong real tasks to do, individual trips or outings, visits to friends or relatives for coffee, actually going to the post office to collect the pension. The list can go on and on and this is where a knowledge of the past lifestyle proves itself. It should also be stated here that the tasks must be real and not ones which do not fulfil the person or are infantilising.

6) Mechanical aids/identification/restraint are all key issues here. Aids such as buzzers on doors, electronic eyes on gates and tagging have, in the past, been mentioned as possible helps with staff control of this problem. However they make no contribution to the dignity of the person's care. Identification cards in pockets or handbags can be useful, although it must be accepted that these get lost of thrown away or lead to a thousand questions as to why the person should have them on their person. Idenity bracelets can also help,providing the person has been in the habit of wearing a bracelet. However these provide more security for staff than help to the resident. The use of 'geriatric chairs' with clip on tables or other restraints can never under any circumstances be condoned.

7) Community assistance, via neighbours, friends of the home, local shops and the police can give a great service in alerting the unit that someone has gone out from the unit unobserved. To this end public relations must be of a very positive nature and this means a sharing of information with people about what the unit is trying to achieve.

8) Every unit should have a procedure when a resident goes missing. Working in a unit which is likely to have some residents who wander requires a clear cut policy laid down in order that all are aware of the action to be implemented. For example:

   - Whole house search. All staff should have 'walked the house' in order that they are aware of all the possible areas in which a resident could 'disappear'.

   - Grounds search. Again staff should know the grounds well.

   - Near street search.

   - Known directional search (when we know the person is likely to head for the same place).

   - Notify family.

– Notify police (full description and photograph helps).

It should be clearly understood that we have no right to restrain residents and to do so could be considered an assault. If residents are such a danger that they require restraint this would fall under the provisions of the Mental Health Act and appropriate medical intervention must be sought. It is essential that all records and the documentation in the case of the wandering person's activities are as detailed as possible.

9) If we know that the resident is likely to wander we have a duty to ensure that the families are fully aware of our procedure in such cases. We need to involve families in reviews on residents and seek their help in ensuring that the care offered is as individualised as possible. The whole range of risks and options must be fully explored as well as how strategies or lack of them will affect the resident. We have to learn to listen to the families and understand how they are affected by seeing their loved one so changed.

10) Sedatives and tranquillisers can assist but they really should be a last resort and only used under medical supervision and with constant monitoring. The effects of their use can hinder rather than help the resident.

11) Following the person is an option. This is an issue which requires full exploration within the staff group. A couple of practical points for consideration here are:
   – Staff should always have access to money for buses or for phoning the unit to advise of their whereabouts. It is not unheard of for a resident to jump on a bus to reach their destination, even though they are 'confused'.
   – Staff must also have access to identification cards indicating where they are employed. The need for this is evident when you consider that our resident could stop a stranger or policeman to complain that 'she/he is following me'.

   The 'following' strategy is an extreme one. However, we must be prepared for its use. It is often the case that the person can forget where they are heading and a familiar face or hearing their name spoken by someone can be a sufficient distraction for them to return to the unit. If the resident leaves by one door and the staff member by another a 'chance' meeting at the main gate or in the driveway can also serve to distract. We should at all costs avoid the situation where two staff members go running out of the unit to catch and bring back the resident as such confrontation only leads to problems for all concerned.

Aggressive Behaviour

Aggressive behaviour may occur occasionally during the course of many, if not most, individual's illness. Several factors may be related to its appearance (and cessation). In general violence is a response to a perceived threat; it may be an attempt to control someone or something or a consequence of frustration. It is made more likely by deterioration in the part of the brain that enables people to inhibit impulses or to think out problems. Often, it is helpful to think about recent changes if someone who is not usually aggressive starts to become violent.

These questions may usefully be considered as possibly contributing to an understanding of an aggressive act.

1) Has something in the environment recently changed? This might be a change in routine, staff members, location, attitudes, level of stimulation, absence of friends, invasion of privacy.

2) To whom is the aggression directed? Is it only one person, or anyone who comes near, or anyone in a uniform, or is it random?

3) When does it occur? In the evening when tired, at mealtimes or when a specific procedure or activity is occurring.

4) Where does it occur? When only two are present, in a specific room, only at home?

5) Are there warning signs? If so, what are they and what happens then? Are these signs always followed by a violent act? If not, what happens after the signs, that is different, when a violent act is averted?

6) What occurs as a consequence of the violent act? Does it always happen?

7) What function does the violent act serve? Does it keep people away or under control or does it ensure attention? What might it be drawing attention to?

8) What skills or procedures might be developed to avert the violent act? What need of the individual is being frustrated and can it be satisfied?

Miss M was an inpatient on an assessment ward. She was suffering from dementia. She sporadically shouted loudly across the ward; someone would usually respond by talking to her, either asking her to be quiet which led to an apology and often a 'making-up', culminating in a cuddle. This was obviously a strong reinforcer and the behaviour increased. When asked what happened if there was no response made, staff felt they could not ignore Miss M because when they had done this in the past she had got 'worked up' and ended up hitting or knocking other patients so they cuddled her to avoid this happening. It seemed possible that Miss M was jealous of other patients when she saw them being attended to. However, the consequences included a degree of hostile response from other patients and some criticism from staff. An analysis of the situation led to the staff deciding to cuddle or talk to Miss M just *before* she started to shout, satisfying her needs for attention and relationship, but reinforcing appropriate or quiet behaviours rather than antisocial ones. Eventually the programme was faded out and Miss M was able to maintain more positive relationships; she then went to a residential home, where she settled successfully.

In this case, Miss M had still a good and sympathetic relationship with others, which could be built on. Often, however, aggressive behaviours make positive relationships difficult so there is sometimes a potential for the aggressive behaviour to escalate. In these circumstances, when the behaviour causes severe strain, an analysis of the situation by an outside agent e.g. a clinical psychologist may be helpful. Stokes book (1987) *Aggression* provides further detailed information.

Issues of 24-hour care

Although 24-hour institutional care is experienced by a relatively small proportion of people with dementia, it must be a major focus for a book such as this because of the extreme vulnerability of elderly people with dementia. Caring for groups of strangers is an activity for which the state takes some responsibility: at the least by the registration of standards in private and voluntary homes. The NHS and local authorities actually provide a good proportion of care themselves although the area of growth is in the private sector.

Day units and permanent care establishments are complex places with complex dynamics. For example if you count all the staff, in a residential home plus the residents, perhaps as many as 80 people are living and working together. To advocate individual expression and self determination is a key aim but as a concept to be practised all the time it is clearly impossible. In these settings the role of the person in charge is crucial. S/he has to recognise the complex dynamics, balance one need against another, prioritise needs and keep the whole place operating positively. Within this balancing act is the constant change of the abilities and needs of someone with dementia and the temptation to do too much for them. Maintaining the view that the person with dementia will always be able to do something or make some choices is very hard work but must not be lost.

Many issues arise in these settings and are to a degree relevant for day care settings too.

1) Segregation/integration

This debate is about whether to provide 24 hour care of people with dementia separately or mixed up with other frail elderly people. (It is illegal to mix the care of elderly people with young chronic sick. See Chronic Sick and Disabled Persons Act 1970.) This is one of those issues which depend crucially on particular circumstances such as the degree of behaviour disturbance, the size of the group, the staffing, the building and the wishes of the individuals concerned. It is possible to have really disadvantaged groups of people with dementia isolated within mixed homes; it is also possible to have disturbance caused by those with dementia diminish the quality of life of all the residents. The emergence of specialist units, both residential and nursing homes, has shown the excellent care that can be provided by highly trained and motivated staff. Many settings are able to provide for a small group of people with dementia as a unit within a larger establishment. Some residential staff maintain a mix is advantageous as long as the proportion with dementia does not exceed 30 per cent. Such rules of thumb however are questionable because it depends so much on the behaviour of the person with dementia and the levels of tolerance among other residents and staff. It is the case that the easiest people to care for in large groups are quiet, biddable, sweet natured people with dementia. A mix can work well in the small group setting if there is a workable and harmonious balance of personalities, abilities and disabilities. Residents can help each other and this helps to develop relationships. Small group in this context means 6–8 people.

2) Contracts

Contracts are discussed elsewhere in this book but in the 24-hour or day care setting they are crucially important. They require that needs and problems are identified; intervention and action are planned; identified people will carry out the intervention and time scales are decided with reviews built in. In preparing a contract it is essential to choose the right time, use simple language and assume the positive. Patience is as essential as the need to be imaginative. All the skills of communication must be brought into play. Contracts should involve relatives or key people in the lives of the person with dementia.

3) Involving Carers

The continuing burden of caring for someone with dementia at home, even with adequate support and help, can become so overwhelming that a carer has to consider relinquishing their caring role. Having to face up to this and coming to terms with the feelings and emotions that this will inevitably provoke, can be an exceedingly difficult process.

Residential staff teams need to have a sensitive awareness of the traumas experienced by both the client and their carer, when the time

81

comes to move into full-time care. Sympathetic listening is vital if carers are to be encouraged to express their feelings.

Relatives' groups which provide a forum for carers, ex-carers and staff to meet, can afford a valuable support network. Working through feelings with people who have already had to make the decision to entrust the care of a relative with strangers can help to heal the wounds inflicted by guilt, grief, anxiety and even relief.

People who have been caring for someone with dementia sometimes find that the stress involved exerts considerable strain on their relationship. Frequently ex-carers find that sharing the care of their relative with staff, within the supportive environment of a residential home, aids in the restoration of their previous relationship, once the continual stress of caring is removed.

Ex-carers should be actively encouraged to be as involved with their relatives as they are willing and able to be. A philosophy of 'sharing the caring task' is one which must be cultivated.

Staff members must be discouraged from perceiving their paid caring role as an exclusive right, which precludes others who choose to be involved. Some staff may become resentful of what could be seen as interference. It is therefore of the utmost importance that the staff team is aware of the value of ex-carers' involvment for everyone concerned.

People who move into residential care are insulated from the outside world, often so much so that they become isolated and are gravely at risk of experiencing a total discontinuity the with rest of their lives. This can be particularly devastating for a person with dementia whose life-long memories are usually encapsulated within the first few decades. It is therefore important that residents maintain contact with family and friends so that they do not lose the links which connect the present with their previous lives. To facilitate this, visitors should be made welcome at any time. Ex-carers can help to bridge the void between the present and past simply by remaining involved.

Ex-carers have a diversity of needs. Some are most comfortable with assuming the role of a volunteer, whilst others derive more satisfaction from helping with the more physical care of their own relative.

Relatives of residents must have the opportunity to participate in reviews of individual care plans as this enables them to keep in touch with their relatives' needs, and helps them to identify areas in which they might choose to be involved. Helping with toilet programmes, personal care and physiotherapy for example, can diminish the sense of inadequacy and reinstate a feeling of worth.

Ex-carers who become involved on a voluntary basis, can make a significant contribution towards enhancing the quality of life for residents living in the home. Accompanying residents on outings to local places of interest, the pub or theatre, helping with fund raising activities, barbecues or parties can be deeply rewarding and help to avoid the feeling of redundancy.

Since people with dementia are often unable to verbalise their thoughts effectively, ex-carers can fulfil a valuable role as advocates. Staff must ensure that ex-carers feel sufficiently comfortable to offer suggestions, voice their opinions and to proffer constructive criticisms when they feel necessary, since these comments are likely to represent the closest objective consumer opinion. Developing an environment which is genuinely responsive to carers and their needs is important. Staff teams should always be willing to listen and respond to anything which ex-carers have to say.

Mrs B an 87 year old widow, was admitted to a residential establishment from her married daughter's home where she had lived for approximately 40 years. She was diagnosed as having a moderate degree of dementia as well as having fairly severe arthritis. The mother/daughter relationship had deteriorated intolerably due to the mother feeling abandoned by the daughter and the daughter feeling totally exhausted by her mother's demands. Consequently visiting became very uncomfortable for both. During attendance of the carers' meeting the daughter expressed guilt, sadness, anger and frustration, particularly during the visiting periods as her mother always demanded to be taken home.

The staff suggested a visiting plan for the daughter which included no more than two 30 minute visits per week and each visit was to be accompanied by the key worker and another member of staff. The time was also to be utilised by mother and daughter engaged in a simple activity, either having tea or manicuring the mother's nails. After approximatley one month the visiting became more comfortable, the staff withdrew their presence but suggested further activities so the time was used positively for both. Three months later the daughter announced in the carers' group that she had found her mother again and both were now able to enjoy each other's company and accept the admission.

4) Brochures

Brochures are a vehicle often employed to provide information about residential homes. This would be innocent topic is in reality a major issue, since it is through written material about an individual establishment that principles should be made explicit. Every centre or home must have a statement of aims, how these are to be achieved and practical rules of the unit.

Many brochures are extremely vague and fail to address key issues such as choice, privacy, illness and death.

Style and content are crucial elements. Identification of who the recipient of such information is to be is another issue which is often overlooked. It is important not to fall into the trap of assuming that people with dementia are unable to comprehend written information.

People with multi-infarct dementia often retain the ability to read until comparatively late on in the progress of the disease. However, the reality is, that people who are considering full time residential care are likely to be severely affected by their dementia. Should the brochure be written for carers, to enable them to share this information with the person whom they are tending; or should it be targeted specifically at the potential client. A further consideration has to be the depth of information people need to enable them to make their own evaluation of the unit, in particular to establish if it can meet the person's individual needs.

Most professionals will have developed firm opinions regarding the content of such publications, but it seems an undeniable fact that professional opinion may not match wholly, or even partly, with that of the intended audience which is why brochures are best written in close consultation with residents where possible and with carers.

5) *The mixed economy*

Provision of residential and nursing home care is increasingly a mixed economy with the private sector becoming ever more firmly established though perhaps not yet sufficiently integrated into the total pattern of local provision. Issues of size and location as well as planning the specific nature of provision remain inadequately addressed. Increasingly registration officers of both residential care and nursing homes are trained but not yet sufficiently in the field of care of people with dementia. This reflects a general lack of expertise in this area which at its worst is seen as unimportant because people with dementia are believed to be unaware of their surroundings.

Proprietors will need to discuss with registration officers the most appropriate use of accommodation to provide a good quality of life for confused residents and to be clear about the aims and objectives of their establishment. These aims should be in writing. Issues of integration or separation of confused and mentally alert residents should be considered in relation to all the factors outlined previously.

Support and guidance for all levels of staff particularly addressing the management of difficult behaviour, the use of restraints, locked doors, etc. should be required as an essential component of registration. Particular attention should be given to the ages, qualifications and previous experience of staff left in charge of specialist homes even for short periods.

Proprietors will need advice on the local availability of community support services particularly those of community psychiatric and clinical nurses. They must be clear about the level of difficult behaviour which it is feasible to manage within their establishment given day and night time staffing levels.

Registration officers will need to ensure that complaints procedures can be understood by relatives and other visitors who may need to act on behalf of a resident with dementia. Where there are not independent visitors some voluntary agencies have agreed to offer an advocacy service to residents in private and voluntary homes.

6) Transport

Transporting people with dementia in mini-buses or ambulances is generally seen as bad for them. It can mean tired and thoroughly disorientated people arriving at day units having spent an hour sitting while the mini bus collects other people.

Increasingly staff are realising that mini-buses are potential therapeutic tools. The journeys can be organised to detour round familiar landmarks. The journeys can be part of a reality orientation session.

During the day an outing from a centre or from a long term care establishment can serve two purposes. It can provide a distraction if people are becoming agitated or bored. It can also be used as part of a programme where familiar streets, workplaces, gardens and buildings are visited.

More practically if day centre staff drive the minibus' daily links with families and other carers can be made at the beginning and end of the day facilitating exchange of information, comfort or whatever is needed.

7) Routine

Good centres and establishments for people with dementia will have a programme which suits residents/members and the staff. It must fit the rhythm of the day and yet be essentially flexible. The person with dementia can use routine to orientate, identify landmarks and time-marks but routine must not overtake the life of staff or members/ residents. There should be flexibility to adjust to changes and events as well as to allow – indeed facilitate – individual expression.

8) Sex

Sex in old age is frequently ignored. It is a taboo subject. There is certainly not enough talk about sex and dementia: many people perhaps assuming that sexual desire goes with the other losses. Yet this is not the case at all.

Mr L thought Mrs McC was his wife. Both were widowed and both had dementia. When their public behaviour in the residential home became too sexually explicit for the residents and staff, they were persuaded to restrict this to their bedrooms. The staff thought Mr L. was making the advances and were not sure Mrs McC was entirely happy about them. They decided not to do anything beyond watching carefully. It transpired that Mrs McC was the one making the advances. Mrs McC's brother visited and accepted the relationship.

The staff in the home in which Mr L and Mrs McC are residents have made a special effort over the last couple of years to confront issues of sexuality and talk about them. This makes them able to deal with each situation on its merits and to react calmly and carefully. The key principles are that these residents are adults and if both are consenting and happy then no action is required. If relatives speak to the staff they answer questions and try to keep the discussion low key.

Many people become sexually very disinhibited with dementia, perhaps masturbating in public or making inappropriate demands. Requesting residents to confine their behaviour to their own rooms or a frank talk about when demands are inappropriate usually works.

Friendships between members/residents can lead to sexual relationships. Sometimes someone with dementia can mistake a person of the opposite sex for their dead spouse. Once again ensuring that both parties are happy is the most important consideration. Communication may not be verbal but it is usually possible to tell if one partner is not welcoming what is happening. Many couples in residential and nursing homes do not get on and may welcome opportunities to live apart or to spend a lot of time apart. Assumptions should not be made that married people are both happy.

Homosexual relationships can be even more difficult for some staff to cope with. All the above recommendations apply.

Miss F and *Miss M* were behaving in a sexually explicit way together and the staff in their home could not cope at all. They were split up. Miss M was sent to another home. It transpired that they had both spent all their lives in single sex institutions.

Staff must be able to talk about their reactions to situations like this if the best decisions are to be made for the residents.

Finally two related issues. First the question of male staff bathing female residents and vice versa. Generally residents prefer to be bathed by someone of the same sex. Some genuinely have no preferences. Some prefer the opposite sex. Once again, sensitive communication and careful discussion between the staff is required. Second, the question of sexual abuse. Little is known about the extent of sexual abuse by staff and relatives of people with dementia. Careful observation and sensitive communication is the only way forward.

Spiritual Care
For people who have practised their faith throughout life dementia need not prove a barrier. Appropriate worship, joining in singing hymns, and saying prayers out loud can overcome the difficulties of aphasia and bring reassurance at a deep personal level. A ministry of spiritual care for people of all faiths should be accepted and assistance sought from the families in locating the familiar minister, pastor, rabbi, or imman. Facilities for worship include ablutions in some faiths. Neuberger (1986) has useful background information.

Medication

All too often the busy doctor consulted about difficult behaviour will succumb to the overriding temptation of seeing an instant remedy for the problem, rather than taking the time to listen to either the person with dementia, or their carer. Invariably the result of this is a hurriedly written, often ill thought out prescription for some form of tranquilliser, sedative or hypnotic medicine.

Once a medicine has been started, its continued administration is often perpetuated by carers themselves; the wife whose husband wakens the whole household during his nocturnal wanderings; the resident whose agitated or aggressive behaviour exerts a disruptive influence on others living in the home; staff who zealously believe that everyone should be 'tucked up' and sleeping at nine p.m. each evening. One does not need a vivid imagination to understand how such situations develop or are indeed perpetuated especially when the effects of such problems initially appear to diminish with the introduction of medication.

The practice of prescribing and administering medication to modify difficult behaviour or exercise social control is alarmingly widespread. Invariably it occurs as a response to meet the needs or demands of stressed carers.

Such practices have developed due to lack of insight into the specific problems associated with the dementing process. This can be further compounded by some carers' inability to identify what triggers off a specific behaviour. If the cause can be identified the situation can often be remedied.

There can be no doubt that people who have dementia are vulnerable. They are people who are socially devalued; whose voices are often inaudible and whose needs and rights go unrecognised or overlooked. By virtue of these factors, people who have dementia are at risk of being condemned to an existence under the influence of medication, and are all too often afforded no choice, other than to be passive recipients of less than mediocre care.

Sedative, tranquillising and hypnotic medicines are capable of exerting a powerful influence over the life of an individual. In addition, medication can have many undesired effects.

Most of the sedative, tranquillising and hypnotic medicines can potentially exaggerate the dependence of an individual on their carers. Thus, tasks which could be achieved with only minimal supervision required intervention from others. Some medicines cause drowsiness and exacerbate confusion which effectively diminishes an individual's awareness of their surroundings' augmenting the problems of disorientation. Other medicines can cause dizziness, tremor or an unsteady gait. These effects may restrict mobility, and contribute to falls or urinary incontinence. Some dampen self motivation which can be attributed to the loss of self care and daily living skills. Hypnotics may cause 'hangover' effects, in itself a cause of insomnia. Yet another undesired effect can be constipation which may further add to confusion. Clearly, it is quite possible to turn a confused, but otherwise fit person into an apathetic individual whose life can become one continuing round of being got up, washed, dressed, fed, toileted and put to bed. The result is a quality of life which can diminish to an unacceptable level. Tending a person who has no quality of life is demoralising and uninspiring. It is difficult to find enthusiasm to look after someone who appears to do little more than sleep. The 'caring' becomes dull and mundane and can be perceived as a thankless chore.

There is no doubt that medication has been and continues to be, used as an unacceptable substitute for skilled, imaginative care. However, developing the expertise and an environment which is conducive to minimising medication is a difficult and demanding process, whether it be for a relative caring for someone at home or an entire staff team within a residential unit.

Residential homes which are managed in a traditional paternalistic style will be unable to cultivate an environment which is conducive to meeting the needs of residents in an individualised way. If medication is to be reviewed with a view to reduction, a major revision of care practices must be orchestrated.

Many professionals and certainly most informal carers perceive medicines to be an infinitely complex subject which is shrouded in mystery, whose secrets are reserved for doctors and pharmacists.

It is true to say that it is a highly specialised area, however, it is important to realise that one does not need to possess an extensive pharmaceutical knowledge to simply question the validity of the use of medicines. Clearly, it is helpful to have an elementary understanding of the purpose for which a medicine is being prescribed: the effect that is desired from a specific medicine, and possible side effects that it may cause. Even a simple understanding can help to untangle the web and demystify some of the complexities.

The aim must be to cultivate and maintain an informal, homely, yet stimulating environment which enables each of the residents to achieve and maintain their optimum level of independence; where each is able to lead as normal and as satisfying a life as possible.

Diminishing the use of medication can be a very fundamental change in practice for any establishment. Such a revolution presents the whole staff team with a major challenge. To effect a change of environment, attitudes and philosophy that enhances rather than detracts from the quality of life for each individual and which ultimately facilitates review and reduction of medication, is a task which requires careful planning and tenacity.

The orchestration of attitudinal and environmental change must be finely tuned to ensure that it occurs in concert. Consultation, planning, identification of clear aims and objectives that are monitored and evaluated, are intrinsic elements throughout the process. Enlisting and establishing commitment is essential, and must include not only the staff team, but also general practitioners and other professionals.

Managing Volunteers and Staff

Volunteers

Volunteers can provide invaluable assistance by extending the range of care available and by increasing th extent of one to one care in particular. Normal recruitment procedures are required such as an interview and the taking up of references. There should always be a contract agreed between the volunteer and the supervisor covering the time to be worked, the type and place of work, and a telephone number.

Training and support must be provided. Matching the skills of the volunteer to the task is crucial. Volunteers are useful in any setting and the list of ways they can be involved is endless.

Often carers who have lost their relative wish to be volunteers. Issues of their personal loss must be resolved before voluntary work is taken up because boundaries can become skewed.

If volunteers are helping with the care of people with dementia, either in the community or in residential settings, it is very important that they are clear about their role. For example, they need to be instructed not to proffer advice about such things as medication, nursing practice or diet. There should be clear instructions about handling clients' money, both in relation to cashing giros and pensions and in relation to shopping on clients' behalf. Volunteers should be helped to recognise depression and the need for more expert counselling than they can offer. They should be especially warned not to brush aside distress with cheerful exhortations. They also need instruction about how to recognise an emergency and how to summon help. It is important that any organisation using volunteers should take advice about any necessary insurance cover.

Staff need to recognise that however altruistic the volunteers' motives they will only continue to make a valuable contribution if they receive encouraging feedback and some opportunity to develop their skills. For example, some kind of support group for volunteers to enable them to share their experience and anxieties may be helpful. They should be encouraged to learn something of their particular residents' backgrounds in order that they can share and discuss early life experience or perhaps eventually embark on really valuable reminiscence sessions.

Staff

The job of care assistants, which in real practical terms is very complex and demanding, usually has only manual worker status and a narrowly defined job description. The job necessitates having workers who are ptient, sensitive, imaginative, caring and intelligent. Caring in itself is not enough. An awareness of ageing, dementia, group dynamics, family dynamics, an ability to be a catalyst and be open minded are just as important. An effective key worker system maximises the skills of staff and creates great job satisfaction which in turn benefits residents.

Regular group and personal supervision are essential. Work programmes should aim towards continuity particularly as shift patterns may isolate some members of staff from colleagues. The job should be time limited because burn-out is almost inevitable in intensive personal care of people with dementia. Workers should change at least every three years. Staff should be encouraged to move on positively.

Volunteers and staff can work in harmony but volunteers have the same needs as staff for:

1) Clear role description.

2) Support: a key person to link to.

3) Regular review of job and performance.

Multi-racial Residential Care

The degree to which Britain is now a multiracial society may not be recognised until a person is admitted to hospital, residential care or day care. White residents may make offensive remarks to black care staff and white staff belittle the needs and customs of elderly from ethnic minorities. Staff need to be on the alert for racist attitudes from fellow residents. If the issue of racism exists in whatever way it must be confronted as soon as possible and not left to fester. This is easier within a regime where facing up to and frankly discussing problems is the norm. Officers in charge have a particular responsibility to work towards harmonious acknowledge of differences while ensuring that a non-racist policy is implemented.

Design Factors

Every effort should be made to ensure that the layout of the centre/home is easy to understand and get around. This is a complex issue which cannot be dealt with in any depth here. Colour coding, different types of decor, large clock with day and date as well as time all help. Clear identification of rooms is essential such as the W.C. Each residents room should have a large name plate bearing their name or, if they are no longer able to read, a useful symbol on the door and should be intensely familiar inside. Individual arrangements and decoration should reflect individual taste, lifestyle and history. Public rooms should have different and very obvious functions: too many uses of the same room can be very confusing.

Possible Tasks for a Key Worker
This list of possible tasks for a key worker ranges from simple to complex:

Newspaper reading/clothing attention/purchase of items.

Arranging optician/dental appointments.

Room arrangements.

Remembering birthdays, special events etc.

Orientation to unit for client/relatives.

Introduction to others.

Clothing inventories/history compiling.

Recognition of personal possessions.

Oversight of physical hygiene.

Maintenance of continence.

Dietary observation.

Records/reviews: instructions to others maintained.

Close involvement of relatives.

Encouragement in participation/communications.

Build-up of 'lost contacts' re church/community etc.

Awareness of expressed/unexpressed spiritual needs, and ensuring appropriate response.

Compiling a lifestyle chart on resident, and assisting in preparation of all reports, for other professionals, on the resident.

Terminal Care
It is impossible to generalise about whether any establishment should care to the end. The decision must be made in the light of the needs of the dying person, the needs of the other residents and the ability of the staff to cope. Clearly the wishes of the person with dementia and their family should be met as far as is possible. Staff should be ready and willing to discuss death either with individual residents or the group so that wishes for arrangements are known. It can be very helpful to raise this issue during a regular review. If possible a room should be made available for relatives to stay overnight when someone is dying.

Chapter 10

Concluding Remarks

This book began as a book for social workers written by social workers and it has grown into a book for all the non-medical workers with people with dementia. Contributors come from diverse professions and settings and the book has grown in weight as well as weighty material. This field of work is developing so fast that new enthusiasts who wish to contribute come forward every day. This book can only be as good as our collective experience in the middle of 1989. This book needs to be cosntantly added to and revised. It is immensely reassuring to find so much enthusiasm and commitment to this complex and often very stressful field of work. In spite of a lack of resources, this enthusiasm and commitment gives hope for the future. It is a future in which we will experience very major changes as the chronic illnesses of elderly people are wrested from the NHS and put into the mixed economy of health and welfare. This is yet another reason why we need a revised volume before too long.

Appendix i

Bibliography

Association of Carers, *Help at Hand*.
Age Concern, *Your Rights*, published annually.
Age Concern England, *The Law and Vulnerable Elderly People*, 1986.
Age Concern England, *Working Together*, 1988.
Age Concern Scotland, *Reaching out to Dementia Sufferers and their Carers*, 1986.
Anton-Stephens, D., *Social Work and Mental Health*. A Guide for the Approved Social Workers. (Ed. Rolf Olsen) Tavistock, 1984.
Bannister, Sir Roger, *Brain's Clinical Neurology* (5th Edition) revised by Sir Roger Bannister, Oxford University Press, 1978.
Bhaduri R., 'Ethnic Elderly', *Insight*, 26.2.88.
Bland R. E., *Residential Care: Is It For Me?* Age Concern Scotland and HMSO, 1987.
British Association of Social Workers, *Code of Ethics for Social Work*.
British Psychological Society, Division of Clinical Psychology *Responsibility Issues in Clinical Psychology and Multi Disciplinary Teamwork*, 1986.
British Psychological Society, *Code of Conduct for Psychologists*, 1985.
Booth T., 'Camden Shows the Way', *Community Care*, 26.2.87.
Carer's National Association *Help at Hand*
Cohen D. and Eisdorfer C., *The Loss of Self: A Family Resource for the Care of Alzheimer's Disease and Related Disorders* Norton & Co., 1988.
Corden J. and Preston-Shoot M., *Contracts in Social Work*, Gower, 1987.
Disability Alliance *Disability Rights Handbook*, published annually.
Gibson F., *Reminiscence: A Training Pack*, Help the Aged, 1989.
Gilleard C. J., *Living with Dementia*, Croome Helm, 1984.
Griffiths Sir R., *Community Care: An Agenda for Action*, HMSO, 1988.
Gwyther L. P., 'Stages of Symptom Progression in Alzheimer's Disease' *Care of Alzheimer's Patients: A Manual for Nursing Home Staff*, American Health Care Association, 1985.
Health Education Council, *Who Cares, Information and Advice for those caring for a confused person*, 1986.
Holden U., Martin C. and White N. *24-Hour Approach to the Problem of confusion in Elderly People*, Winslow Press, 1983.
Hughes R. D. and Bhaduri R., *Race and Culture in Service Delivery*, DHSS, October 1987.
Jaques Alan, *Understanding Dementia*, Churchill Livingston, 1988.
King's Fund Centre Project Paper No. 23, *Living Well into Old Age*, King's Fund Publishing Office, 1986.
Mace N. L. and Rabins P. V., *The 36-Hour Day*, Hodder and Stoughton, 1985.

Marshall M., *Social Work with Old People*, British Association of Social Workers/Macmillan, 1983.

Murphy E., *Dementia and Mental Illness in the Old*, Papermac, 1986.

Neuberger J., *Caring for Dying People of Different Faiths*, Lisa Sainsbury Foundation, 1986.

Norman A., *Severe Dementia: The Provision of Long Stay Care*, Policy Studies in Ageing No. 7 from The Centre for Policy on Ageing, 1987.

Occupational Therapists Board, *Infamous Conduct*, Obtainable from The Council for Professions Supplementary to Medicine.

O'Hagan K., *Crisis Intervention in Social Services*, British Association of Social Workers/Macmillan, 1986.

Oliver M., *Social Work with Disabled People*, British Association of Social Workers/Macmillan, 1983.

Pulling J., *The Caring Trap*, Fontana, 1987.

Rimmer L., *Reality Orientation Principles and Practice*, Winslow Press, 1982.

Scottish Action on Dementia, *Dementia in Scotland: Priorities for Care, Strategies for Change*, 1986.

Scottish Action on Dementia, *Dementia and the Law: The Challenge Ahead*, Discussion Paper prepared by the Rights and Legal Protection Sub Committee, 1988.

Scottish Health Education Group, *Coping with Dementia: A Handbook for Carers*, 1987.

Stokes G., *Aggression*, Winslow Press, 1987.

United Kingdom Central Council for Nursing, Midwifery and Health Visiting, *Code of Professional Conduct for the Nurse, Midwife and Health Visitor, 2nd Edition*, 1984.

Walsh K. W., *Neuropsychology: A Clinical Approach*, Churchill Livinstone, 1982.

Contributors

Charles Barker
Assistant Director
Services to Older People
Tameside Social Services
Department

Daphne Barnett
Registration Officer
London Borough of Lewisham

Reba Bhaduri
Social Services Inspector

Rosemary Bland
Lecturer in Social Work
University of Stirling

Sarah E. Colles
Specialist Health Visitor in
Psychogeriatrics
Royal Edinburgh Hospital

Lindsay Colburn
Officer in Charge
Avon County Council Social
Services

Audrey Derrick
Senior Assistant (Elderly)
Somerset Social Services
Department

Alison Froggatt
School of Applied Social Studies
University of Bradford

Susan E. Garner
Head Occupational Therapist
Prestwich Hospital

Faith Gibson
Senior Lecturer in Social Work
University of Ulster

Valerie Good
Community Services Manager
East Sussex County Council
Social Services

Jean Kewley
Health Visitor, Liverpool

Jan Killeen
Director
Scottish Action on Dementia

Audrey Lees
Chairman
London Region Alzheimer's
Disease Society

Marsh Marshll (Editor)
Director
Dementia Services Development
Centre
University of Stirling

Carol Martin
Principal Clinical Psychologist
Leeds Western Health Authority

Kathleen McManus
Director
Whitecross Nursing Home,
Dundonald

Susan Newton
Senior Social Worker
Liverpool Personal Service
Society

Michael O'Reilly
Director
Knowesouth Nursing Home
Jedburgh

Beryl Pain
West End Carers' Support
Scheme
Newcastle Upon Tyne

Raphael Phipps
Co-ordinator
The Moss Side Afro Caribbean
Care Group for the Elderly and
Infirm

Michael Preston-Shoot
Senior Lecturer in Social Work
Manchester University

Linda Robinson
Dementia Scheme Co-ordinator
Age Concern Northern Ireland

Bob Sapey
Deputy Principal Officer
Elderly and Handicap Team
St. Austell

Joan Scrine
Visiting Lecturer in Social Work
and Handicap
University of Kent

Malcolm Smith
Assistant Director of Social
Work
Western Isles Council

Kath Stephenson
Training Officer
Liverpool Social Services
Department

Jenny Tate
Senior Principal Social Worker
Royal Edinburgh Hospital

Alan Tatham
Top Grade Clinical Psychologist
Salford Health Authority

Glenda Watt
Officer in Charge
Residential Home for the Elderly
Edinburgh

John Wyllie
Area Care Manager (East)
Church of Scotland

Evelyn Gibb typed and circulated all twelve drafts of the texts as well as the final copy. The Editor wishes to record grateful thanks for this heroic effort. Without her willingness to persevere with the task of incorporating the contributions with such skill, this book would not have been possible.

Appendix iii

List of Organisations

Carers National Association
29 Chilworth Mews
London W2 3RG
(Tel: 01 724 7776)

Alzheimer's Disease Society
158/160 Balham High Road
London SW12 9BN
(Tel: 01 675 6557)

Alzheimer's Scotland
33 Castle Street
Edinburgh EH2 3DN
(Tel: 031 225 1453)

Age Concern England
Bernard Sunley House
60 Pitcairn Road
Mitcham
Surrey CR4 3LL
(Tel: 01 640 5431)

Age Concern Wales
4th Floor
1 Cathedral Road
Cardiff CF1 9SD
(Tel: 0222 371566)

Age Concern Northern Ireland
6 Lower Crescent
Belfast BT7 1NR
(Tel: 0232 245729)

Age Concern Scotland
54a Fountainbridge
Edinburgh EH3 9PT
(Tel: 031 228 5656)

Help the Aged
16 St James Walk
London EC1R OBE
(Tel: 01 253 0253)

Scottish Action on Dementia
33 Castle Street
Edinburgh EH2 3DN
(Tel: 031 220 4886)

Index